ANIMAL BEHAVIOUR

ANIMAL BEHAVIOUR

J. L. CLOUDSLEY-THOMPSON

M.A., Ph.D. (Cantab.), F.R.E.S., F.L.S.

Professor of Zoology, University of Khartoum
Sometime Lecturer in Zoology, King's College, University of London

NEW YORK

THE MACMILLAN COMPANY

1961

First Printing

Printed in the United States of America

Library of Congress catalog card number: 61-14635

To my mother and father
who first taught me
to behave,
and
to my wife and children
who have continued
the good work

Acknowledgments

MY THANKS are due to the Editors of *Discovery, The New Scientist, Science News* and *School Science Review* for permission to use material from articles of mine that have previously appeared in their pages. I would also like to thank Dr N. Tinbergen for his advice, Mr T. G. Usborne for a number of stimulating philosophical discussions and for drawing my attention to the quotation from La Fontaine, Mr Frank W. Lane for the use of photographs, Miss Dilys G. Thomas and Mrs C. A. Morrison for secretarial assistance. Mrs Morrison has also helped by her careful perusal of the manuscript. For the opinions expressed and any of the inadequacies of the book, I alone am responsible.

Some of the drawings are original, others are based on photographs or on drawings by N. Banks and T. E. Snyder, F. E. Beddard, L. A. Borradaile, F. Boulière, M. Burton, K. von Frisch, W. E. Garrey, H. Hediger, T. W. Kirkpatrick, G. F. Makkink, G. Nixon, C. F. A. Pantin, B. B. Roberts, F. S. Russell and C. M. Yonge, A. E. Shipley, M. Smith, N. Tinbergen, M. Vachon, W. M. Webb and C. Sillem, to which authors acknowledgments are here made.

Preface

THIS VOLUME arises from a series of London University Extra-Mural lectures. Herein I have attempted to explain simply the modern approach to the study of animal behaviour. Information has been borrowed from many sources, some of the more fruitful of which are listed in the bibliography; but I hope to have achieved more than a series of plagiarisms. By selection of topics I have tried to show that the behaviour of animals is primarily concerned with keeping in the right kind of environment, obtaining food, avoiding enemies and synchronising reproductive activities. The complex interactions between physiology and environment that form the basis of behaviour in higher forms have been analysed and illustrated by comparison between the simple reactions of lower animals, the rigid instincts of insects, fishes and birds in which learning is comparatively unimportant, and the more plastic type of behaviour found in mammals which culminates in human insight.

Much of the fascination of ethology lies in the fact that a synthesis of objective and subjective approaches, however desirable, is really impossible. But the juxtaposition of these incompatibles provides an endless source of variety and interest.

J. L. C-T.

April 1959

Foreword

by

KENNETH MELLANBY, C.B.E., Sc.D.

Head, Department of Entomology, Rothamsted Experimental Station
and President, Association for the Study of Animal Behaviour

IN recent years there has been a great increase in interest in the subject of animal behaviour. Our popular newspapers are filled with anecdotes of the sagacity of their readers' pets. Writers with the smallest amount of knowledge and experience do not hesitate to develop theories attributing superhuman powers of reasoning to the lowest animals. At the same time the number of authoritative books on animal behaviour has also increased, so that the serious student is likely to be overwhelmed by the volume of material presented to him. It might be thought that yet another book on animal behaviour was superfluous. I do not believe this to be the case, and would like to give an especial welcome to Professor Cloudsley-Thompson's latest book.

'Animal Behaviour' has many points which I should like to commend. First, it is written in such a way that an intelligent reader with no specialist knowledge of biology will be able to understand it; it is free from the obscure jargon which makes some books on this subject incomprehensible to all but the expert. Secondly, although the author includes the results of many other workers, he illuminates his text in a refreshing way by accounts of his own observations on animals and man in such a way as to make the reader feel that he has been taken into his confidence. Thirdly, although the book is easy to follow by the non-specialist, the serious student of animal behaviour may also learn much from it, for it contains accounts of experiments and observations from an unusually wide field, and many professionals have restricted their observations to small groups of animals so that they may have missed the wider implications of their work. Finally, the facts are allowed to speak for themselves, and no preconceived theory is thrust upon the reader. He is left to make up his own mind on the theoretical implications of the subject, and he is likely to be stimulated himself to make more careful observations on the behaviour of animals—and of himself.

In many scientific subjects today the amateur and the professional are becoming widely separated by technical barriers. In the study of animal behaviour this need not be the case. Professor Cloudsley-Thompson shows the amateur who is willing to accept the standards and discipline of the professional that he too can make observations which may advance the frontiers of knowledge, and thus he may help to solve some of the problems raised in this book.

Contents

Photographic Plates

Chapter 1

Survival in a hostile world

> Wherefore one should not be childishly contemptuous
> of the most insignificant animals. For there is some-
> thing marvellous in all natural objects.
>
> ARISTOTLE (384–322 B.C.)

IT IS WELL to start at the beginning. And in the beginning, we are
told, God created light. At any rate, it is fairly clear that the
universe cannot have existed for ever, and it does not seem improbable that it may have begun in the form of highly radioactive
energy many million years ago.

Questions of time and distance are among the most difficult
confronting astronomers, on account of the indirectness of the
methods of measurement that have to be used beyond any but the
nearest stars. Furthermore, different methods must be employed
at increasing distance.

The fact that the universe as a whole seems to be expanding in
that the more distant nebulae appear to be receding from one
another at speeds proportional to their mutual distance, can be used
as a basis for calculating its age. Since the time when it was in a
very highly compressed form, somewhere between 9,000 and
18,000 million years may have passed. The evidence from isotopic
abundance, the composition of terrestrial and meteoritic leads, the
A^{40} content of the atmosphere and so on, indicate that the earth
itself is about 5,000 million years old.

The origin of life

Life depends essentially upon the unique properties of the
combining powers of three elements and the infinite diversity of
phases and systems made possible by the properties of water. By
the relations between these, the pathway from simple compounds
to complex organic bodies is made direct. Notwithstanding, the
transition between a non-living organic combination and a similar

one that is alive embodies the greatest and most incomprehensible of all biological mysteries.

It is believed that life may have begun over 500 million years ago. If this time scale were represented by the height of Cleopatra's Needle, the thickness of a penny placed on top would represent about 40,000 years — the length of time during which man has been in existence. The thickness of a stamp stuck on to the penny would indicate the infinitesimal proportion of time during which he has been civilised!

Some biologists believe that life began in the depths of the ocean, others in layers of molecules absorbed on colloidal clays in soil water, or in layers on air-water interfaces. Certainly the surface of the early earth could have given rise to a variety of organic compounds, ready to give up their energy in a number of different reactions. The theory which most appeals to me is that it began in the surface waters of the oceans. Here there was abundant energy in the form of ultra-violet light, and comparatively stable temperature and salinity. Conditions were anaerobic, mineral and metallic catalysts abundant.

Now plants obtain from sunlight, in the presence of the green pigment chlorophyll, the energy with which they synthesise carbohydrates from carbon dioxide gas and water. The chlorophyll acts like a catalyst and speeds up the reaction which would otherwise take place very slowly indeed. Nevertheless it *would* take place to a certain extent even though no chlorophyll were present. Indeed, this may still be happening, but any organic matter thus produced would quickly be oxidised or devoured by bacteria and other micro-organisms.

It would not matter how slowly the reaction took place 500 million years ago, for the world was sterile and there were no living microbes to break down the complex organic compounds so laboriously synthesised. As the centuries passed, the surface waters of the primeval oceans may have reached the consistency of soup, for proteins as well as carbohydrates would have been produced. When life began, it would have spread like wildfire in the presence of this abundant food.

There are two points in favour of the surface-water theory which it may be as well to mention. The first is that today much of the ultra-violet light which comes from the sun is absorbed by the ozone and oxygen in the atmosphere before it ever reaches the earth. Most of this oxygen has been produced by green plants as a

2

by-product of their photosynthesis and the ozone is formed from this photochemically and is therefore a secondary product of the photosynthesis, so that in the days of which we are speaking the intensity of ultra-violet light reaching the waters would have been very much higher than it is today. The second point is concerned with the salinity of the primeval seas in which life began. According to geological estimations, the primitive ocean contained more potassium and less magnesium than is present in modern sea water. Since that time, the composition of the water has been gradually changing on account of the precipitation of various compounds on to the bed of the sea. When life evolved, the salt content of the sea water was probably very similar to that of the blood serum of modern animals.

Now if, as we believe, the conditions under which cell life is possible are very restricted and have not altered substantially since life began, it does not seem unreasonable to suggest that life would never have begun unless conditions had once been as I have described. Today, the blood of marine animals maintains within the organism by various physiological mechanisms, an environment with the properties required for the continued life of its cells.

By the time the influence of ultra-violet radiation on the course of events had become insignificant because of the formation of an ozone layer in the upper atmosphere, enough free energy would have been stored in the mass of organic molecules in the sea to keep evolution going until photosynthesis developed and free oxygen became available in quantity.* Before this, however, the evolution had occurred of highly complex self-duplicating units and the discrimination in favour of one set of optical isomers from a pair of equally probable asymmetrical molecules.

Life on Mars

Let us digress for a moment to consider the possibility of life on Mars.

For planetary life to develop, certain conditions must be present. These include water in a liquid form, a suitable rotation period, low orbital eccentricity, favourable chemistry of air, water and

---

* It is interesting to speculate that if life on earth were exterminated, it could never again follow the same course. Not only did each link in a chain of improbable reactions occur while favourable conditions lasted, but these events prevented their re-occurrence. For example, there has been a steady loss of hydrogen into outer space, ultra-violet penetration to the surface of the earth has been greatly reduced and free oxygen has appeared in the atmosphere.

rock, and a steady star as a source of energy. Among catalogued stars there are about 40,000 like our sun, and there must be innumerable others in the various galaxies. Indeed it has been estimated that there are probably not less than 100,000 million planetary systems in the cosmos. It seems unlikely that our own should be unique.

On the other hand, in view of the conditions necessary to produce life, it is apparent that only Mars, Earth and Venus of the planets in our solar system are within the proper temperature range. Mercury is too hot, Jupiter and Neptune too cold. The surface of Venus is concealed by impenetrable clouds but the atmosphere consists largely of carbon dioxide, with no measurable amount of oxygen or water. It is therefore unlikely to support living organisms.

The latest theory on the 'canals' of Mars is that they are natural, disconnected surface faults. The surface of the planet is difficult to study because it is frequently clouded with dust, but the atmosphere is sufficient to afford protection from the impact of meteors and cosmic rays.

For a long time it has been known that there are green patches on Mars which have been observed to wax and wane. Their colour has recently been shown to agree spectroscopically with that of terrestrial lichens. Even if life in the form of lichens does exist, it is unlikely that higher plants or animals can do so because the climate must be exceptionally severe. Possibly some Arctic animals might survive for a while if transported to this inhospitable planet, but I do not think it is possible that they could pass through entire evolutionary history under such conditions any more than they have done on earth. Indeed, Arctic forms have probably exploited the colder regions of the world comparatively recently.

There remains the possibility that there may be, elsewhere in the universe, other forms of life entirely different from anything we know on earth. This is exceedingly improbable, I think, because spectrographic analysis has not revealed elsewhere in the universe any elements not known on earth; and even if there were any, their chemical qualities could be predicted from their position in the periodic table. Of all the elements, only one, carbon, possesses the ability to form complex organic compounds which readily associate with other substances — like haemoglobin with oxygen for example. Reactions involving carbon are unstable at high temperatures and take place infinitely slowly at very low temperatures.

4

Hence life could not exist under climatic conditions markedly different from those on this earth; but I do not doubt that it appears wherever conditions are favourable.

The nature of behaviour

Conditions are by no means favourable everywhere even on earth and every living thing is somehow adapted for maintaining itself in suitable surroundings. For example, even bacteria show some sort of behavioural responses, and will not enter a drop of acid placed in their culture medium.

In essence, behaviour is the response of living matter to some form of stimulus, although the response can be affected by many variables. The simplest type of behaviour consists of automatic or 'reflex' maintenance activities, so-called because their function is to maintain the animal in a suitable environment.

It can be shown experimentally that the whole surface of an *Amoeba* is sensitive to stimuli such as chemicals, light or heat. The protoplasm of the animal responds by protruding the '*pseudopodia*' used in locomotion and it reacts to food particles by the formation of a temporary mouth. The *Amoeba* therefore possesses all the fundamental qualities of behaviour. It is irritable, conductive and, in the absence of external disturbance, rhythmic: for the emptying of the contractile vacuole which regulates the water content of the protoplasm and reproduction by cell division are both rhythmic processes. But in this primitive organism the reception and transmission of stimulation and the response achieved by means of the effector organelles are all blended.

In other Protozoa, however, behaviour is often determined by structural features such as flagella, cilia, shells and so on. The Ciliates, of which *Paramoecium aurelia* is a well-known example, possess '*neuroneme*' fibres for the conduction of stimuli and '*myonemes*' by which the shape of the body is altered. The Metazoa are republics of co-operating cells which become specialised for different functions and as we ascend the evolutionary series, we find the gradual development of a brain, the Parliament which controls the activities of other parts of the body.

Directiveness and purposiveness in behaviour

Before discussing this subject in detail, there is a philosophical problem which needs mention. It is the relationship between 'directiveness' and 'purposiveness' in behaviour, for much of animal behaviour conveys an appearance of purpose. By analogy with our own feelings, we naturally tend to regard such 'purposive' actions as the result of the 'will' which brings them about through the agency of the brain, nervous system and muscles. This point of view contrasts with the essentially mechanistic outlook that the biologist derives from purely physiological and morphological studies, according to which behaviour is interpreted in terms of reflex arcs, chemical and electrical changes in the nervous system, and so on. Yet Protozoa possess apparently purposive behaviour and this is effected without brain, nerves or synapses. The 'synapse' or junction of one nerve fibre with another, like the nerve-muscle junction, acts as a valve so that it allows an impulse to pass in one direction only. Indeed, 'purposive' behaviour is merely a type of response executed by different types of machinery in different cases. Electro-chemical changes along the surface of a cell and the production of chemical substances such as hormones are the two methods exploited by living organisms. Adrenalin and acetylcholine which are so important in the vertebrate synapse also occur in Protozoa, whilst electro-chemical waves of activity are found in some plant cells although their function, if any, is at present unknown. Perhaps they are simply concomitants of the structure of protoplasm which have been exploited by the animal kingdom.

In the field of behaviour there are two cardinal errors to be avoided in the interpretation of observations. The first is known as *anthropomorphism* and involves the subjective implication of human thoughts and emotions in the analysis of animal behaviour. *Teleology*, the second, is the assumption of 'purpose' instead of directiveness in the behaviour of an organism.

It is clearly unsatisfactory to say that the heart beats *in order to* keep up a flow of aerated blood. It is equally, though perhaps not so obviously misleading to claim that bees visit flowers in order to get food or conversely that flowers have evolved bright colours in order to attract bees. If there is any purpose, it is to be found, not in the animal, but in the mind of its Creator. And that lies not in the realm of Science but of Theology.

We may feel that the behaviour of a dog expressing pleasure or disappointment recalls our own feelings in like circumstances. There is a tendency, however, to read a similar but simpler mental life into the actions of lower animals. To imply a consciousness into a creature as different from man as an ant or termite, as has frequently been done in the past, is intellectually dangerous. It would be equally logical to imply consciousness to our own vital organs or even to the cells of which they are composed. The study of animal behaviour has often been complicated and impeded by falling for this insidious temptation.

Introspection enables us to realise that our behaviour is partly controlled by foreknowledge of goals and ends, but even human behaviour is dependent upon physiological mechanisms which have to be studied experimentally to be understood. Hence terms like 'anger', 'fear', 'hunger' and so on are merely guesses as to the possible subjective state of an animal. We may use them for convenience and simplicity, but always with this reservation.*

Maintenance activities

From a biological point of view, perpetuation of the species takes precedent over survival of the individual whose importance is merely that of a reproductive unit. The object of a flea, insofar as it can be said to have one, is to produce more fleas, and so on. When a clash occurs between the requirements of individual safety and protection of the young, parent animals will frequently sacrifice themselves so that their offspring may escape. In certain cases, too, individual animals may give their lives for the good of their social unit or colony. Soldier ants and termites, for example, will fight to the death in defence of their nest, and a bull elephant of his cows.

Nevertheless, much of the existence of an animal is concerned with self-preservation. This aspect of life is reflected in the many facets of behaviour that are collectively known as 'maintenance activities', and which range from simple posture responses to complex feeding activities and escape reactions.

Protozoa: *Amoeba proteus, Arcella vulgaris* and *Paramoecium caudatum* (greatly enlarged)

* 'Alone among the creatures, man can look upon himself and become the object of his own thoughts, can distinguish the world he knows from himself as knowing it. In the exercise of that faculty he transcends the limit of mere matter.' Mgr. R. A. Knox (1888–1957).

7

They are common to all animals, helping them to withstand the rigours of a hostile world. We shall conclude this chapter with a brief resumé of some of the most important types of maintenance activity, before passing on to consider in greater detail the mechanism of such behaviour.

Position responses

Some of the simplest position responses arise from the need of creeping animals to maintain a foothold and when this is lost there is a righting reaction which results in re-establishing contact with the substratum. Thus if an *Amoeba* is suspended in a drop of water, it sends out long, slender '*pseudopodia*' in all directions until the tip of one comes into contact with a solid surface, spreads out and becomes attached. The remaining pseudopodia are then withdrawn into the body and the animal glides on to the surface, resuming its normal shape. This type of response is even more marked in a related form, *Arcella*, which has a dorsal, limpet-like shell and ventral pseudopodia. In *Hydra* the righting response is clearly a reaction to contact, but mere foothold is not sufficient as the animal requires space in which to spread its network of tentacles. It therefore moves about, alternately detaching its basal region and attaching its tentacles to the substrate, after the manner of a leech or looper caterpillar, until this condition is fulfilled. The righting reactions of planarian worms, star-fishes and brittle-stars have also been studied in detail and result in the ventral surface of the animal coming in contact with some solid object. It is very doubtful whether gravity plays any part in the orientation of these animals which readily come to rest at any angle from the horizontal. Species that live buried in sand or mud however, such as many worms and bivalve molluscs, take up and maintain a particular

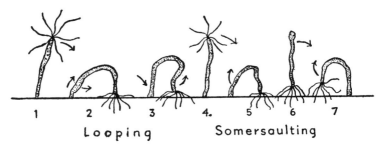

1   2   3   4.   5   6   7

Looping   Somersaulting

Movement in *Hydra*

8

position with respect to the surface of the medium. Here responses to gravity are also involved since the animals must be able to find their way to the surface should they become too deeply buried.

Animals that swim or fly, and to a lesser extent those that walk and run, have constantly to maintain and adjust their equilibrium and their orientation to gravity. Most crustaceans have special sense organs which serve not only for hearing but also for balance, while certain species which lack them usually orientate themselves to light by turning their backs to it. Optical sense organs have important stimulatory effects known as 'phototonus'. When the two eyes of an insect are illuminated unequally there arises a loss of tone in the muscles on the darker side. The asilid fly, *Proctacanthus*, for example, becomes immobile or makes feeble unco-ordinated movements if its eyes are painted over. In the dark or with blackened eyes its legs collapse, but in the light it raises its body well above the ground. If one eye alone is blackened, tonus is exaggerated on the uncovered side and different regions of the eyes have been shown to have varying degrees of importance in the tonus of different groups of muscles so that the insect takes up characteristic attitudes when only part of its eyes are blackened. The eyes of vertebrate animals, including man, have a stimulatory function as in invertebrates.

Finding and remaining in a suitable environment

Many animals can survive only in limited and restricted habitats which they find and remain in by means of their behaviour reactions. Often the young and adults inhabit similar localities but in other cases the offspring are placed in an environment suitable for their development by the action of their mother. Female insects, for example, usually lay their eggs in localities where there

Phototonus in the fly, *Proctacanthus* sp.

9

is suitable food for the larvae and are attracted to such places by sight, touch or smell. In the case of drifting marine larvae, however, distribution by shifting currents may be quite haphazard and only a small proportion of the young is swept into areas suitable for further development. It is probable, even so, that in most cases larvae do not settle or anchor themselves unless the substrate is favourable to them and this increases their chances of survival.

Light is one of the most important factors of the environment to which animals respond, thereby maintaining themselves in favourable situations. The factors involved in the orientation of animals to light vary greatly in different groups. In *Amoeba*, for example, the response is brought about by reflex inhibition of the formation of pseudopodia on the more highly illuminated side; in *Paramoecium* it depends upon changes in direction of the stroke of the hairlike '*cilia*' by which the animal swims, while in worms random movements correlated with rapid changes in the intensity of illumination on the light receptors are responsible for orientation. In insects and spiders, however, orientation is brought about by a series of co-ordinated automatic reflexes in the legs or wings which are correlated with the stimulus of light on the eyes and ocelli. In all these forms orientation results in movement towards regions that are favourable to the organism. In the higher animals and in certain insects such as ants and bees this frequently occurs without apparent orientation. They can go towards any given point in space, with any part of the surface of the body ahead and also whilst continuously changing the part which is ahead.

An interesting example is afforded by the behaviour of ants when taking food to their nests. If the food particles are small the ants pick them up and carry them, walking forward; but if the particles are too large the ants drag or roll them, walking backward or sideways. When crossing obstacles they often climb nearly vertically upward and downward and frequently fall, rolling over and over. But no matter what impedes their progress, they continuously proceed in a given direction. Recently it has been shown that whereas some species of ant follow odour trails from the nest, others respond to polarised light. Nevertheless, there is a parallel between the behaviour of a foraging ant and that of higher animals which has not yet been fully elucidated. In man, memory and reason are involved: there is no satisfactory evidence that reason plays any part in the behaviour of insects.

Another interesting reaction is shown by many aquatic animals which orientate themselves in accordance with the direction of water currents. Thus the planarian worm, *Crenobia alpina*, shows a response by which it crawls upstream before its eggs are laid. Everyone knows that fishes in a stream spend much of their time head on to the current, keeping station at a particular spot. If they did not do so, sooner or later they would be swept away into the sea. But this is only indirectly a reaction to the water current because in fact the animals can be shown by experiment to be responding to their visual surroundings. Only if it comes to rest on

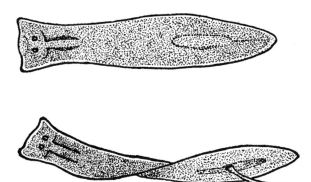

The flatworm, *Crenobia alpina* (length about 5 mm)

the bottom can a fish *feel* the water flowing over its body. In a wide and deep stream of uniform velocity any fish must be moving with the current, so there can be no differences of pressure on different parts of its body. Without some point of reference which is at rest relatively to the stream (supplied by tactile or visual perception of the banks or bottom) it is impossible for the fish to react to the current in any way. Similarly a bird on the wing cannot be aware of the strength and direction of the wind unless it can see the ground below; and locusts and mosquitoes will fly against the wind only if its velocity does not exceed their own speed: they settle unless they can move in a forward direction in relation to the ground above which they are flying.

Food-finding activities

In the simplest animals feeding activities are elicited in response to simple stimuli. *Amoeba* finds non-mobile food by means of a chemical sense while mobile prey is perceived through the vibrations it sets up in the water. In *Hydra*, chemical stimuli serve to sensitise the stinging cells whose poisonous, barbed threads or *'nematocysts'* are discharged on contact with the prey. Any small animals that come in contact with the network of tentacles these creatures possess are stung and eaten. There is no active directed search for food and no pursuit of the prey.

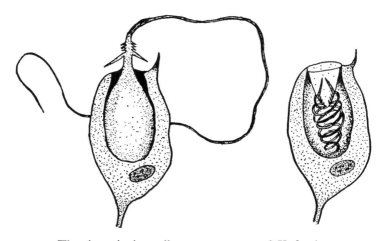

The tiny stinging cells or nematocysts of *Hydra* (enlarged). The one on the left has been discharged

Predatory species usually react only to animals of size suitable to form their prey. Thus large web-spiders do not respond much to vibrations of small amplitude and high frequency. These attract smaller spiders since they are the type of stimulus set up by smaller insects caught in their webs. Conversely smaller spiders are not attracted by vibrations of lower frequency and higher amplitude such as attract their larger brethren, for in general small insects have high wing-vibration rates while larger species have lower rates of vibration. Similarly, relative size is an important factor in the recognition of prey by animals that hunt by sight.

There is little to be gained from a mere catalogue of the types of sign-stimuli to which 'hungry' animals respond — the scents and colours by which vegetable and refuse eaters recognise their food and the many visual, tactile and chemical stimuli that excite the predatory forms. It is of greater interest to study food-seeking from an ethological point of view. In man, for example, physiologists have found that food-finding is a highly integrated muscle action caused by a system of nervous motor impulses originating in a higher centre in the hypothalamus of the brain. These can be influenced by external and by internal stimuli which are dependent on contractions of muscles in the stomach wall. These in turn are associated with the subjective phenomenon of hunger which arouses the food-seeking *'drive'*. The difficulty of the scientist in synthesising both subjective and objective, psychological and ethological approaches to the study of behaviour is due to the fact that introspection brings him into a realm that is beyond the reach of objective investigation even though the data gained by it and by objective study are both factual. It is but another aspect of the paradox of 'purpose'.

Toilet

Much of an animal's private life is devoted to grooming and cleaning itself and special organs have been evolved for this sole function. Filter-feeding organisms (p. 69) have evolved sorting mechanisms which prevent their feeding apparatus from becoming clogged and gill-breathing aquatic organisms are endowed with structures for cleansing their respiratory surfaces. The gills of the lobster or crayfish, for example, are contained in chambers through which water is kept flowing by the action of the second maxilla. An appendage known as the *'scaphognathite'*, flapping at the rate of about sixty strokes a minute, bales water forward, out of the gill-chamber and under the opening of the excretory organ beneath the antenna. By this action fresh water is drawn into the chamber between the bases of the legs and harmful particles removed.

Many tunicates, such as *Oikopleura albicans*, an aberrant marine creature distantly related to the vertebrate animals, possess the power of secreting a kind of house many times the size of their body. This is only loosely attached, however, and is thrown off as soon as it has become clogged through straining nutritive and other particles from the large volumes of water which filter through its complicated passages and perforated folds.

Insects and arachnids spend much of the time cleaning their appendages. After a meal, spiders and harvestmen can be seen to clean their mouthparts, passing palps and limbs through their jaws. Since the prey is digested externally by means of enzymes it is essential that the several channels and grooves in the mouthparts should be kept free from solid particles. Insects not only clean their mouthparts but groom their whole bodies, brushing themselves with their legs. I have sometimes noticed a cockroach rubbing itself backwards and forwards against a piece of paper as though scratching a tickle. Social insects are especially prone to cleaning themselves and in addition indulge in social toilet activities in which they rub, pat and massage one another.

Fishes and newts can be seen to rub their bodies against aquatic vegetation, frogs wipe their mouths with their feet and reptiles which have indulged in sticky meals such as slugs and snails will rub their noses against plants in a manner similar to that of a bird cleaning its beak after feeding. It is well known that large crocodiles sunning themselves on a mud-bank hold their jaws agape whilst the spur-winged plovers clean their teeth for them!

Cleanliness is most important to birds whose wings deprive them of a pair of limbs with which to scratch. The heron has a 'powder-puff' on its breast. This consists of short, brittle feathers coated with a waxy powder. At the same time the middle toe is serrated like a comb. After a meal of eels and other slimy fish, the bird dips its head into the 'powder-puff' which soaks up the slime: then it grooms its beak and feathers with its middle claw. The importance of this ritual is shown by the fact that the bill of an injured heron, which had only one leg and therefore could not clean itself, was so choked with slime and fish scales that the bird was unable to swallow.

Many birds will take any opportunity to bathe themselves in fresh water or indulge in dust baths. Such activities may tend to discourage lice and other ectoparasites, as does preening, but seem to be indulged in chiefly for the 'pleasant' sensation they give. Furthermore, exposure to sunlight of oil from the preening gland situated above the tail, facilitates the synthesis of vitamins. The enriched oil is then swallowed during subsequent preening activity. The curious phenomenon of 'anting', in which various species of birds have been seen to place live ants among their feathers and sometimes even to roll among ants, may be an exaggerated form of the same type of behaviour.

Most mammals devote long periods to their toilet and mice are said to spend up to half their lives cleaning themselves! Mutual grooming is an important factor in maintaining the association of social species and valuable salts may be obtained when animals lick each other. Cattle can often be seen to assist each other to clean inaccessible parts: standing head to head they lick each others head and neck. In addition to their duties as sentinels, African tick-birds relieve buffalo, rhinoceroses, elephants and antelopes of their annoying parasites. It would be interesting to know to what extent parasitism and mutual grooming have contributed to the evolution of social behaviour among mammals.

Escape from enemies

Whether or not the hunted fox suffers fear we shall never know, for fear is a subjective phenomenon that can only be discovered by introspection. What, however, is readily observable is that many animals, including the fox, flee from their enemies hoping to elude them by speed and agility, or react to imminent danger by im-mobility, helped often by protective coloration. Some are able to change colour so that they match their environment, others defend themselves with teeth and claws, spines or stings or depend upon the protection afforded by shell and carapace. Some use bluff to startle their enemies, others resort to *autotomy*, the reflex casting off of a limb or tail that has been seized by an enemy. In the lowest animals, however, the flight response is merely an exaggerated form of the reaction that normally takes them into a suitable environ-ment. *Paramoecium* responds to any disturbing feature in the

Escape reaction of the scallop, *Pecten maximus*

environment by the stereotyped avoiding movements described in the next chapter. Planarian worms show only positive or negative reactions whatever stimulus is presented, but in the higher animals, not only are the methods of escape more diverse, but the perceptions involved are more specific and more clearly differentiated.

For example, scallops, *Pecten* spp., and queens, *Chlamys* spp., react to the presence of their inveterate enemy, the starfish, by flapping the valves of their shells and swimming upwards. Similar escape responses occur in many other marine molluscs. If a starfish approaches a limpet there is no sign of activity until the predator's tube feet make contact with the shell of the limpet. The mollusc

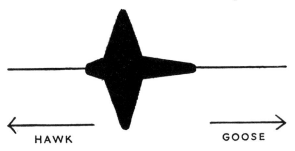

HAWK   GOOSE

A hawk-goose model. When moved to the left above young turkeys and other birds it caused fear reactions, but in the opposite direction it did not disturb them

thereupon raises its shell like a mushroom, wiggles and rocks from side to side, then glides rapidly away. Under such conditions, the starfish does not give any outward sign of recognition. If the predator's tube feet have acquired a grip, however, so that a straight pull does not suffice, the limpet does not clamp down but continues moving about until it has escaped. If it is unsuccessful, it ends up within the stomach of the aggressor.

Once again, however, specific reactions are the response to particular sign-stimuli. Insects and Crustacea with well-developed, compound eyes flee from sudden movements which they are specially adapted for perceiving. Responding to shadows cast upon them, tube-dwelling worms rapidly retract their crown of tentacles; mosquito larvae respiring at the surface of a pond wriggle down to the bottom; the field-vole darts for cover. The reactions of young game birds, ducks and geese to a flying bird of prey are released by the sign-stimulus of a short neck, and comparatively crude models with this character will elicit a response. Other species respond to the scent of their enemies. As mentioned above, the scallop darts away when a starfish approaches: as this escape reaction can be induced by dropping pulped starfish skin on to the mantle cavity it is probable that the stimulus is chemical. Yet other species become aware of approaching enemies by the vibrations they cause. Snakes are highly responsive to vibrations set up in the earth by approaching footsteps and the curious comb-like sense organs known as *'pectines'* attached ventrally to the abdomen of scorpions, serve in the perception of ground vibrations and thus provide warning of danger.

The defence reaction of the toad consists of adopting a peculiar posture in which the animal puffs out its body like the frog in the fable who lost its life by attempting to reach the dimensions of an ox. By inflating its lungs the common toad can increase its size by as much as a half. At the same time the bulky body is raised from the ground and tilted towards the side from which danger threatens. Although this attitude can be evoked by a number of optical and visual stimuli, its chief function is to prevent the toad from being swallowed by a snake. It is not surprising, therefore, that the stimulus most effective in eliciting the defence reaction is the sight of a long, thin object. Consequently, a garden hose has a

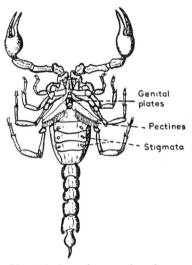

Genital plates

Pectines

Stigmata

Ventral view of a scorpion showing 'pectines'

dramatic effect upon toads! It is only under the influence of strong stimuli that defence reactions are provoked, and it is possible to keep toads as pets for years and yet never witness these peculiar attitudes.

In this chapter no attempt has been made at completeness, but I have tried to indicate by means of selected examples that maintenance activities, on the whole, comprise simple automatic or reflex responses to equally simple stimuli. They come relatively low in the hierarchy of behaviour patterns, which is to be expected, for as we have seen, not even the most primitive organism could hope to survive for long if it took no action whatever to keep itself in a suitable environment. Consequently some maintenance activities must have originated with life itself.

PLATE I

OWL AND PREY.
The owl is a highly specialised nocturnal predator

PLATE II

Mocking-bird attacking a great horned owl
near its nest

Defence reaction of the toad

PLATE III

PLATE IV

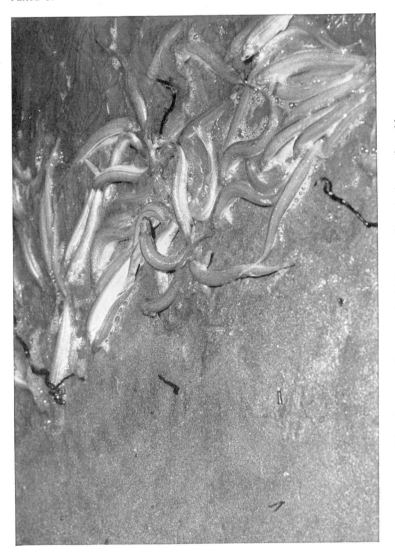

Grunion spawning near the high-water line during spring tides

Chapter 2

The simple behaviour of lower animals

Que la beste est une machine;
Qu'en elle tout se fait sans choix et par ressorts:
Nul sentiment, point d'âme, en elle tout est corps.

. . . .
L'animal se sent agité
De mouvements que le vulgaire appelle
Tristesse, joie, amour, plaisir, doleur cruelle,
Ou quelque autre de ces estats
Mais ce n'est point cela; ne vous y trompez pas.
J. DE LA FONTAINE (1621–95)

IN THE PREVIOUS CHAPTER we saw that behaviour consists essentially of mediated and co-ordinated responses to environmental stimuli. We shall now consider the mechanism of these in greater detail. Bacteria, the simplest of the Protozoa and the free-living unicellular plants respond to stimuli only by avoiding them. None of them possesses many types of reaction and most not more than one or two.

Protozoa

For example, *Paramoecium caudatum*, sometimes known as the 'slipper animalcule', tends to aggregate in regions of weak acidity. This behavioural response is of value to the animal as it lives in stagnant water and feeds on the bacteria that cause leaves to decay. The metabolism of the bacteria affects the medium so that it becomes more acid. Consequently the response of *Paramoecium* to this acidity guides it to a plentiful supply of food.

If a drop of dilute acid is placed in a glass dish containing a culture of *P. caudatum* the responses of the animals can be observed with the aid of a low-power microscope. The *Paramoecium* will be seen to swim at random by means of the fine hair-like '*cilia*' with which their bodies are covered. They enter the acid region purely by chance and not by any directed movement. When they reach the acid-water boundary on the way out, however, they turn and go back into the region of acidity. Within the drop of acid, away from the boundary, they turn little or not at all; but near the boundary the frequency of turning, or *rate of change of direction* increases sharply, depending on the degree of decrease in acidity. This type of response is known as a '*klinokinesis*'.

In *Paramoecium* the avoiding reaction is very clearly distinguished from the normal behaviour of the animal. The more often

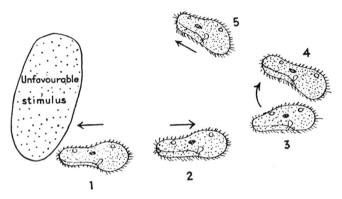

Klinokinesis in *Paramoecium* sp.

it occurs, the less likely the animal is to move away from a particular region and consequently an aggregation of individuals tends to occur there. If a number of animals are taken from a culture and placed in a solution of greater alkalinity, their rate of change of direction will be seen to increase greatly: but gradually the frequency of turning drops as they become adapted to the new medium.

If *Paramoecium* is subjected to stronger stimulation in the form of strong acids or alkali, heat, touch or dilute poisons, it responds by discharging a number of sticky threads known as '*trichocysts*'. In this species, therefore, there exist two types of behavioural response; klinokinesis and the discharge of trichocysts.

Sea anemones

In multi-cellular animals the response varies, depending not only on the nature and strength of the stimulus, but also on the physiological state of the individual. Stimuli too weak to cause an immediate response may be summated to produce one later. Thus if a point on the foot of a sea anemone is stimulated electrically and the contraction of the sphincter muscle which lies round the edge of the disc is recorded, it is found that the response to a single shock is slight or non-existent. If a series of shocks is given at intervals of 0·5–1·5 secs, however, the response to each shock increases gradually. This *'staircase effect'* is interpreted as indicating that each stimulus makes the muscle more sensitive to further stimulation. In other words, *neuro-muscular facilitation* occurs.

A group of sea-anemones

The more quickly the stimuli follow each other, the steeper the 'staircase effect' because facilitation quickly fades from the muscle after the stimulation has reached it. But increases in the energy of the electric shock, provided they exceed the minimum necessary to produce a response at all, have no effect on the staircase. The explanation is that, when nerve cells are stimulated, a propagated impulse is set up either completely or not at all: a partial response is not possible. This is known as the *'all or nothing'* law of conduction.

If the disc of a sea anemone is gently touched, the animal responds by bending the edge of the disc inwards. The reaction gradually disappears, however, as it passes round the disc, but the stronger the stimulation the further it extends before it fades out. At first sight this appears to be contrary to the 'all or nothing' law, but in fact it can be explained in terms of *interneural* facilitation.

The nervous system of the sea anemone is composed of a network of small conducting cells each of which communicates with others by means of one or more *synapses*. The synapse or junction between two nerve cells acts as a barrier across which an impulse may, or may not pass. In the nerve-net of the sea anemone the arrival of an impulse reduces, for a time, the resistance of that

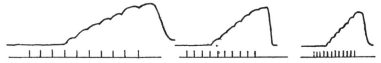

'Staircase' effect in the sea anemone, *Calliactis* sp.

synapse to the passage of later impulses and this is what is meant by interneural facilitation. The stronger the stimulation, the longer is the train of impulses that is engendered and consequently the further the impulses travel. Since the responses of muscle fibres increase when they receive longer series of impulses, however, there is an apparent decrease in the response of more distant muscle fibres.

A nerve-net may be differentiated other than in the facilitation which occurs in various areas. First, the rate of conduction of an impulse may vary in different directions. For example, an impulse may travel at a rate of 4 cm. per sec. through the thickness of the column of a sea anemone, 10 cm. per sec. along the length of the column, and 120 cm. per sec. in the nerve-net of the mesenteries (the vertical folds of the body wall which divide up the interior of the animal). Hence impulses follow some routes more quickly than others. In addition impulses may pass more easily in one direction than in another. Thus if the end of a tentacle is cut off, its circular muscles contract only on the inner side of the cut and the open end of the severed piece remains uncontracted.

The nerve-net of the sea anemone differs in no essential feature from the nervous system of higher animals. Conduction is slow, however, because the nerve-net is peculiar in possessing a much greater number of synapses. Also, facilitation is greater than in other nervous systems. These differences are quantitative rather than qualitative however, and the process of conduction is similar in all animals.

Despite its simple nervous system, the sea anemone is able to show quite complicated patterns of behaviour. The small shrimps, worms and fishes that form its food are killed by batteries of stinging cells in the tentacles and then transferred to the mouth, but inedible and unwanted materials are rejected. It has been shown experimentally that the stinging cells are sensitised by lipoid absorbed on protein in very dilute concentrations — such as is provided by the slime which covers a fish — but their actual discharge is triggered by means of contact or mechanical stimulation.

Thus the nervous system of the animal is closely related to its behaviour. For it is inevitable that any characteristic, whether morphological or physiological, must be related to mode of life in terms of survival value. To give another example; certain shore-living sponges are able to squirt out water for some distance and for long it was not understood what function this had in the lives of the animals. It is now known, however, that hot weather occasionally kills all the sponges except those living in caves and other sheltered places where the water is stagnant. In this type of environment, squirting water removes waste products and enables the animals to survive. And it is their progeny which recolonises the shore waters. Hence the behavioural characteristic can be explained on an evolutionary level.

Worms

When we pass up the animal kingdom to the planarian worms, we find the beginnings of a simple brain and central nervous system in addition to a peripheral nerve-net. This is correlated with the fact that the animal is bilaterally symmetrical and consequently there is a concentration of sense-organs and their nerves at the anterior end of the body.

In segmented or annelid worms, the control exerted by the head region becomes more marked, as the brain is better developed: it controls the muscle tone and sensitivity of other parts of the body, for worms whose cerebral ganglia have been removed tend to be very sensitive and restless. Nevertheless each segment of the body is controlled by its own ganglion in the ventral nerve cord.

If this nerve cord is severed, waves of peristaltic movement can still pass down the body from head to tail and will continue to do so if the two ends are afterwards tied together, even after the body of the worm has been cut in half. This is because each segment is stimulated mechanically by the movement of the one immediately in front.

That earthworms are capable of learning has been shown by means of experiments in which a T-shaped glass tube is used as a maze. One arm of the T leads into a jar containing moist earth and moss as a reward. The other arm is lined with sand paper and contains two electrodes through which a shock of one volt can be administered to the unfortunate worm if it takes the wrong turning. After a hundred or more trial runs, the worm learns nearly always to turn down the arm of the tube that leads to the moist earth and moss!

If the positions of the reward and punishment are interchanged, the worm will unlearn its previous lessons and, after a time, learns to crawl down the other arm of the T-tube. Earthworms can learn even if the entire central nervous system of the first six body segments is removed. Indeed, each segmental ganglion is capable of learning in the same way that the brain learns.

Habituation

The simplest form of learning is known as *'habituation'*. This is the name given to the waning of a response as a result of repeated stimulation. It consists of getting used to, and ignoring stimuli which cease to have any significance in the life of the animal. Habituation can readily be observed in the reactions of a spider to the vibrations of a tuning-fork touching its web. At the first application the spider will rush out and try to bite the fork, but before long it ceases to respond to the stimulus.

Worms are normally very sensitive to vibrations of the soil in which they live. But if the soil is caused to vibrate constantly for a long period, they eventually cease to show any response. In a similar way travellers on board ship cease to hear the noise of the engines and become aware of them only when speed is increased or decreased.

A great deal of what is perceived by the sense organs is neglected. For instance, to take another human example, one can listen to two people talking without noticing an aeroplane passing overhead and traffic on the road. What is perceived is highly selected and, in the case of higher animals, supplemented and given meaning from past experience. Perceiving is governed by many factors, not the least being preconceived notions. Sometimes these are so extreme as to be delusions which may be so strong that they result in a flagrant disregard for obvious facts.

It has been shown that, in man, such delusions tend to appear at moments of anxiety and stress. Nervous or anxious people are far more likely than others to imagine burglars and to have hallucinations of obstructions when driving on a foggy road.

Hallucinary tendencies are cut short as soon as more information becomes available through the sense organs and are created to a smaller extent when anxiety is at a low level. At the same time, preconceived notions tend to be more stable under such conditions. This appears to be so especially when a relatively high level of anxiety has recently been reduced at the end of an arduous task when the more obvious dangers have receded, and may be the cause of many otherwise inexplicable road and rail accidents.

When we speak of an animal as being 'tame' we often mean little more than that it has become habituated to human beings. Walk to the edge of a pond and the fishes swim away as soon as they see you. Now repeat this several times daily, and the response will quickly become less marked. In a similar way, almost any animal except, perhaps, the most primitive can be 'tamed'.

Habituation can be a source of danger to an animal, particularly in relation to traps set by man, and indeed is frequently exploited. Tameness, however, usually implies more than habituation: it may also involve the establishment of a *conditioned reflex*; that is, a reflex modified by experience. To quote the classical example, food placed in a dog's mouth evolves a reflex flow of saliva. If the introduction of food is accompanied by ringing a bell and this is repeated several times, the bell alone eventually stimulates salivation. The original salivation reflex, which is inborn, is not lost as a result of the experiment; the induced response to the bell alone is a conditioned reflex.

When an animal is tamed, it must first become habituated to the presence of man before it can be taught to come to him for food. Furthermore, lower animals learn to recognise, not individuals, but situations. I once had a goldfish who became absurdly tame. He would feed from my fingers in the aquarium and grew so big that I had to put him in the pond in the garden. Alas for any anthropomorphic self-delusions! In his new surroundings he immediately became the wildest of fishes: not until he was re-habituated to my presence at the side of the pond could the necessary reflexes be established for him again to come to me for food. But of fishes, more later.

Rhythms in lug-worms

Research on the physiology of worms, especially the common European lug-worm, *Arenicola marina*, shows that even these lowly creatures may have a useful contribution to make to our understanding of animal behaviour in general. Lug-worms inhabit fairly permanent burrows on muddy beaches. They feed on the sand and mud, digesting some of the organic content and ejecting the residue in the form of worm-casts which may be seen, in thousands, when the tide is out.

The lug-worm, *Arenicola marina*

In the laboratory, the worms are housed in glass U-tubes where their behaviour can be observed. They are able to obtain a supply of water by making pumping movements which can be recorded by means of a float attached to a needle writing on a revolving drum. It might be thought that under constant environmental conditions the behaviour of the animals would be regulated entirely by their physiological state: that they would feed until their stomachs were full, then make a backward trip to the surface to evacuate the rectum, and so on. But this is not so. They feed in little bursts of only a few minutes' duration, with rests in between. If no sand is present, a similar pattern of feeding movements can be observed, each of which subsides although there has been no satisfaction by eating. Backward movements to the surface also occur at intervals of about 40 minutes, even though there are no residues to discharge.

This observation suggests that lug-worms have some spontaneous 'physiological alarm clocks' in their organisation which initiate behaviour patterns irrespective of the animals' needs. It is clear, therefore, that the behaviour of lug-worms involves more than a series of reflex responses to stimuli from the environment.

The 'alarm clock' responsible for the feeding rhythm has been located in the oesophagus. If the front part of the gut is removed and placed in a dish of sea-water, it will show the same rhythm. In the entire animal this rhythm is transmitted to the muscles of the proboscis and thence to the body wall. In other species of lug-worm, the central nervous system rather than the oesophagus appears to act as a 'pace-maker'.

The lug-worm is a creature of 'moods' and has several alternative patterns of behaviour which can be employed according to circumstances. If the surface water at low tide becomes dangerously hot or cold, or diluted with rain water for example, it is wiser for the worms to suspend their activities for a while. But, under the influence of the forty-minute rhythm they make periodic trips to the surface and test the water, resuming full activity when the rising tide has covered their burrows again and so removed the danger.

Similar innate rhythms play an extremely important part in animal behaviour especially in relation to the cycle of day and night, discussed in a later chapter.

Insects and spiders

In spiders, insects and other Arthropoda, behaviour consists of elaborate chains of reflex responses, either instinctive or conditioned by learning, similar to, but more complex than those of the Annelida. Conduction along the nerve cord is improved as there are fewer synapses and the reflexes usually involve two or more segments, as occurs in walking. The brain is enlarged and more elaborate: it is the main centre for the reception of stimuli from the sense organs and central control is correspondingly greater.

The arthropodan brain is also an important inhibiting centre. If the head is removed, co-ordination is lost, but a headless insect can still run about or lay its eggs, for different ganglia are responsible for the actions of different parts of the body. Furthermore, the brain is the controlling centre for rhythmic activities.

Thus it can be seen that behaviour is largely built up of local reactions co-ordinated by the brain. Instincts are composed of elaborate chain reflexes centred in, initiated and controlled by the brain. In subsequent chapters this analysis is extended and the influence of learning is considered; but ultimately it will be seen that behaviour is reflected in the structure and function of the brain as the central co-ordinating organ in the animal's body.

Chapter 3

Life on land

DESPITE THE INSTABILITY of its climatic conditions, dry land offers many advantages to the animals that have been able to adapt themselves to terrestrial life. The possibility of rapid movement, a copious supply of oxygen and protection from aquatic enemies represent but a few of the advantages gained by migrating to land. Terrestrial life entails a number of problems, however. There is an ever-present danger of water shortage, larger animals require additional structural support, respiratory organs must become adapted for breathing air and there is no surrounding water into which toxic excretory compounds can diffuse.

The conquest of the land by insects and other arthropods illustrates a number of fundamental points of behaviour in the responses of animals to the simple stimuli provided by their physical environment. Discussion of the physiological adaptations of vertebrates to terrestrial life provides an example of the ways in which the study of morphology, physiology and behaviour supplement one another. No other group rivals these two as successful land animals because none has succeeded so well in adapting itself to the terrestrial habitat.

The conquest of the land by insects and their relatives

The distribution of animals is determined not only by the physical conditions of the environment — light, temperature, moisture, wind, acidity or alkalinity and so on — but also by its biotic factors which include plants and other animals. In the present chapter, however, we shall be concerned only with interpreting the distribution of terrestrial animals in terms of their physiological responses and behavioural reactions to the former. The significance of these at once becomes apparent when one remembers that life probably began in the sea, a relatively stable environment and not subjected to violent changes in temperature or salinity. In this medium were evolved all the major groups of animals and during succeeding epochs most of them managed to conquer the land to a greater or lesser extent.

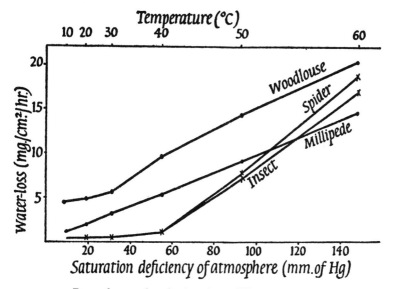

Rate of water-loss in dry air at different temperatures, and corresponding saturation deficiencies, of a wood-louse, millipede, spider and insect. In the woodlouse and millipede the rate of water-loss is proportional to the saturation deficiency of the atmosphere, but in the spider and insect it is negligible below about 35° C, the critical temperature at which their epicuticular wax-layers become porous. Rate of water-loss is expressed in milligrammes per square centimetre of surface area per hour

Small animals have a very large surface area in proportion to their mass; consequently the conservation of water and the maintenance of a fairly constant internal medium are especially important to terrestrial forms. Many land invertebrates such as insects, spiders and mites avoid becoming dried up by covering themselves with a thin layer of wax which is relatively impervious to water vapour. Unfortunately such a layer is also impervious to oxygen and carbon dioxide. A respiratory mechanism has therefore had to be evolved which permits gaseous exchange to take place whilst restricting water loss to a minimum. The spiracles of insects and the lung-books of spiders and other arachnids are normally kept closed by means of special muscles, and only when carbon dioxide in the body begins to accumulate are they opened to facilitate respiration. It can easily be shown experimentally by weighing that the rate of water-loss by evaporation from an insect or arachnid is greatly increased when 5 per cent carbon dioxide is present in the atmosphere, as this results in the respiratory apertures remaining fully open. Before moulting takes place a new wax layer is secreted beneath the old cuticle that is due to be cast off, so that the ecdysis is effected with a minimum loss of water.

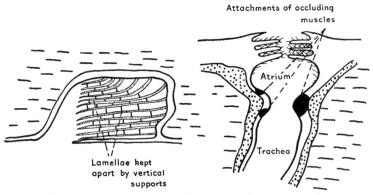

Lung-book of a spider (left) and spiracle of a butterfly larva (right) as seen in section

In addition to such morphological and physiological adaptations to life on land, insects and arachnids have evolved special excretory products — uric acid and guanine respectively — which are extremely insoluble. Consequently nitrogenous waste matter can be eliminated from the body in a dry state and no water is lost in the process.

A second method of avoiding desiccation on dry land is found in woodlice, centipedes, millipedes, springtails and many other small animals which remain most, if not all of the daytime in a damp or humid environment under stones, fallen leaves, and in crevices under the bark of trees. When taken into the open they are stimulated by light and drought so that they run actively until, by chance, they reach some dark damp spot where they come to rest. They can run directly away from light, but one searches in vain to find any directed orientation toward moist air or damp surfaces. The animals run aimlessly, turning first one way then the other. But, as the air becomes damper, their speed decreases.

The behaviour of woodlice can be illustrated by a simple analogy with motor cars. Suppose a procession of cars is travelling at a steady speed of 50 m.p.h. outside a town. On entering the restricted zone the speed falls to 20 m.p.h. which is retained through the urban area. Now it will be seen that the cars are closer together. The time interval between the passage of one car and the next will be the same throughout the town and the country but, because they move more slowly in the built-up area, they will automatically be closer together. So it is with woodlice which move more slowly and consequently aggregate in damper air.

In addition to this simple '*orthokinesis*' or variation in linear velocity, woodlice tend to turn more and more frequently as they pass through a zone of moist air, until they finally come to rest. This is a '*klinokinesis*' similar to that found in *Paramoecium caudatum* and discussed in the previous chapter.

It is by such purely mechanical reactions that woodlice aggregate under bark and stones. Experiments have shown that the animals are not in any way attracted towards one another. They merely gather in the same place as a result of behaviour reactions which drive them away from light and from dry places.

Woodlice also show a diurnal rhythm of activity and tend to wander abroad during the night, when the temperature drops and the humidity of the atmosphere increases. This rhythm is correlated with alternating light and darkness and not with fluctuating temperature and humidity although these factors of the environment are probably of greater importance in their daily lives. This can be explained by the fact that changes in light intensity are more consistent and reliable throughout the year. Consequently it is not surprising that light often acts as a token stimulus which leads animals to a place where other environmental conditions are favourable.

A decrease in the intensity of the humidity response at night enables woodlice to walk in dry places where they are never to be found during the day. On the other hand movement away from light becomes more marked in animals which have been in darkness for some time. This ensures that they get under cover promptly at daybreak and thus, no doubt, avoid the early bird. But if their daytime habitat should dry up they are not restrained there until they die of desiccation, since their response to light is reversed in dry air so that they are able to wander in the open until they find some other damp hiding place and again show a negative response to light.

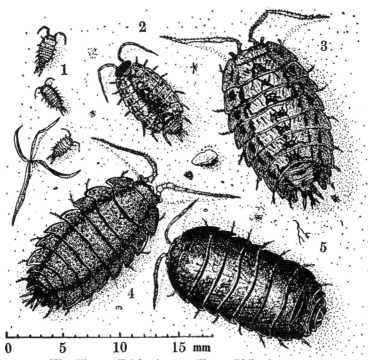

Woodlice: 1. *Trichoniscus pusillus*, 2. *Philoscia muscorum*
3. *Oniscus asellus*, 4. *Porcellio scaber*, 5. *Armadillidium vulgare*

All woodlouse species tend to lose water *comparatively* rapidly in dry air. The most resistant in this respect is the pill woodlouse, *Armadillidium vulgare*, which can survive in the open for several hours. Next in the series comes the common *Porcellio scaber*, easily recognised by its rough, granular integument, then the garden slater, *Oniscus asellus*, and finally the smaller *Philoscia muscorum* which soon dies from desiccation when exposed to dry conditions. All species must spend the greater part of their time in an atmosphere that is saturated with water vapour, but there is considerable variation regarding their ability to withstand dry air, high temperatures and in the period of time during which they can venture into dry places. *Ph. muscorum* has been shown to be the most intensively nocturnal in habit, *A. vulgare* the least. So it is probable that the degree of nocturnal activity is correlated with the ability to withstand water-loss by evaporation.

Somewhat similar responses have been shown to occur in

millipedes which also lose water rapidly in dry air. Some species may tend initially to move towards dry places but the reaction is gradually reversed as desiccation proceeds. Orientation is again entirely '*kinetic*' or non-directional and in an experimental chamber in which a choice of humidities is provided, both the time spent and the distance covered are greater on the moist side.

Spotted snake-millipede, *Blaniulus guttulatus*

The response of millipedes to moisture has some economic importance, for under conditions of drought they may be forced to attack growing crops for the sake of water. Thus outbreaks of the 'spotted snake-millipede', *Blaniulus guttulatus*, tend to be stimulated by a dry spell following a period suitable to the reproduction of the species when the soil is damp, undisturbed and rich in humus. It has been shown experimentally that humus and rotting substances have a texture which is preferred by millipedes to that of living plant tissues, and that the animals are attracted to dilute concentrations of sugars.

No doubt a moist season combined with the use of farmyard manure or following some crop producing a considerable amount of humus, will engender a great increase in the number of millipedes in the soil, particularly if the ground is not disturbed by ploughing etc. They may be beneficial at this stage in aiding the breakdown of the humus, but if the following season is dry, even for a short spell, they may be compelled to attack crops for the sake of moisture. Once an attack has been initiated, the attraction of sugars in the plant sap will prevent them from returning to their normal diet of humus and decomposing matter. It is unlikely that damage by millipedes to crops with tough exteriors such as potatoes and mangolds can ever be primary, for not only do their weak mouthparts prevent them from gaining access, but in addition they are not attracted to unbroken skins of potatoes, only to cut surfaces. Once an entrance has been achieved, however, through mechanical damage or the bites of wire worms and other pests, the millipedes will eat out the entire centre of a potato and the damage they cause

33

is often followed by fungal attack. Furthermore, the fact that single potatoes have been found containing over a hundred *Blaniulus guttulatus* of all ages while the remainder of the crop was unharmed shows that they must have been attracted to a damaged tuber and could not have bred there.

Like woodlice, millipedes avoid the light, but with the exception of a directed response or *'taxis'* in those forms that possess eyes, their reactions are non-directional. When illuminated they crawl around until, by chance, they find themselves in darkness where they come to rest.

Although to millipedes, as to woodlice, humidity is the most important factor of the environment, as we have seen, these animals are not able to find their way directly to damp places: instead, they are merely repelled kinetically by drought. Nevertheless this stereotyped and curiously negative behaviour is surprisingly effective in preventing them from wandering away from their normal habitats: but it does raise the problem of how dispersal can take place and new habitats become colonised.

There are a number of cases on record of millipedes, sometimes accompanied by centipedes and woodlice, migrating in vast armies. Occasionally they have crossed railways and been squashed in such numbers that locomotives have been impeded and sand has had to be strewn on the lines before their driving wheels would grip. At other times cattle have refused to graze on invaded pastures, wells have been filled with drowned corpses and workmen cultivating the fields have become nauseated and dizzy from the odour of millipedes crushed by their hoes. Such mass migrations, however, are of rare occurrence and local in extent, so that their net effect on distribution is probably negligible.

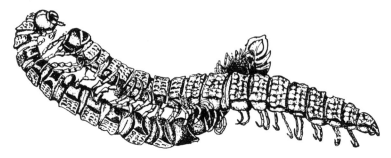

Flat-backed millipedes of the family Polydesmidae in the mating position

34

The explanation of the problem of distribution probably lies in the fact that, as already mentioned, the restraining mechanisms are somewhat relaxed during the night when the temperature falls and the humidity of the air increases. Thus it is at night that these creatures are enabled to disperse themselves and overcome the restrictions inherent in the physiology of the integument.

It would be a mistake, however, to regard the absence of a cuticular wax-layer as a primitive characteristic, although the forms that lack one are so restricted in their choice of environment that they cannot be regarded as entirely successful land animals. Rather, it seems that different methods have been exploited for surviving the conditions of life on land.

The conquest of the land by the ancestors of woodlice and other terrestrial arthropods probably took place across the littoral zone, for shore-dwelling species are still the most primitive in structure. Now animals crossing this zone may well be subjected to high temperatures, and the ability to lose heat by evaporation of water may have had considerable survival value. These ancestral forms were probably at first all restricted to damp environments by their behaviour mechanisms. Later some of their descendants, such as modern woodlice, centipedes and millipedes exploited still further this form of terrestrial life, while others, the insects and arachnids, acquired waterproof integuments and the other physiological and morphological mechanisms that must accompany them; but all this is pure speculation. In the absence of direct evidence comparative physiology can merely suggest the kind of course that evolution may have followed.

The general speeding up of life in a medium of abundant oxygen and negligible viscosity has resulted in increased specialisation of the central nervous system, and only the size limit imposed by respiratory requirements and the necessity for growth by moulting may have prevented the arthropods from dominating the terrestrial environment to an even greater extent — possibly even to the exclusion of the vertebrates, including man.

The conquest of the land by the vertebrates

The history of the conquest of land by the vertebrates is a very different one from that of the invertebrate animals. Not only was a different route followed, but different physiological and behavioural adaptations must have taken place. Lungs and legs are the most

35

characteristic features of terrestrial vertebrates, but these must have been developed *before* the animals migrated to land.

The mud-skipper, *Periophthalmus* sp. among mangrove roots

The actual stages by which fins evolved into legs have not been preserved as fossils, but some modern fish, such as mud-skippers, *Boleophthalmus* spp. and *Periophthalmus* spp. show how well comparatively unmodified fins can act as limbs. Mud-skippers scramble about on mud and mangrove-roots with the aid of muscular fins which are bent under the body like legs. The bat-fish or frog-fish, *Malthe vespertilio*, which inhabits the shallow water of the West Indies also crawls on its pectoral fins. It is said to assume a toad-like attitude when on land, the head pointing slightly upwards and both pectoral and pelvic fins acting as limbs. The fins of the fishy ancestors of the Amphibia must have been somewhat similar although they were not used for hopping. It is probable that they were lobed and were first used on land as levers as their owners wriggled along. Initially they can have carried little weight, but gradually they became elongated and turned under the body, raising it from the ground.

Associated with the conversion of paddle-like fins into elongated, jointed legs there must have been corresponding changes in the structure and function of the pectoral and pelvic girdles to take the strains and stresses of this new mode of locomotion. In recent amphibians, such as newts and salamanders, the pectoral girdle has become secondarily reduced, whilst in frogs, where the fore-limbs serve mainly to take the shock on landing from a jump, the pectoral girdle shows a degree of fusion of its constituent bones.

The first steps towards the development of lungs were probably taken long before limbs showed any modifications useful for life on land. The explanation of this pre-adaptation lies in the fact that

36

lungs arose in response to life in the stagnant waters of tropical swamps. Originally perhaps a mere recess in the gullet richly supplied with capillaries, the primitive lung must soon have developed as a sac with abundant blood vessels and a simple wind-pipe down which air could be forced. Later this was converted into the swim-bladder of fishes which acts partly as a hydrostatic organ and partly as a pressure indicator.

Every period of severe drying-up of land water must have witnessed the extinction of vast numbers of fishes. Two evolutionary alternatives only were available; to go back to the sea or forward on to the land. Most fishes went back and recolonised the oceans, competing favourably with the heavier cartilaginous sharks, rays and dogfish which had never acquired a swim-bladder. A few enterprising forms, however, succeeded in the conquest of the land. Some of their descendants evolved into modern lung-fishes: others are the ancestors of the tetrapod vertebrates.

Osmotic regulation and water conservation

As we have seen, the ancestors of the terrestrial vertebrates must have migrated to fresh water before moving to the land. A change in the salinity of the environment raises problems of 'osmosis' — the movement of water across a semi-permeable membrane towards a stronger solution. The maintenance of a proper internal medium and blood composition is a relatively simple task for marine animals because the composition of internal media and sea-water are not strikingly different, even today. But as soon as animals began to move towards fresh water, far reaching changes in their regulatory mechanisms became necessary.

Crabs, lobsters, worms and other invertebrates which live near the shore or in brackish water can tolerate small changes in the salinity of their blood, but in more highly organised forms the limits of toleration are lower. So migration to fresh water had to be accompanied by refinements in the fish kidney to cope with the increase in the amount of water that had to be excreted. The presence of a 'glomerulus' in the kidney of marine as well as of fresh-water teleosts or bony fishes, is evidence of a fresh water ancestry. This has degenerated in marine forms, but persists in fresh-water fishes. In the cartilaginous or elasmobranch fishes, a high blood concentration of urea has been evolved as an alternative method of water conservation.

In marine teleosts there must be a constant danger of desicca-

37

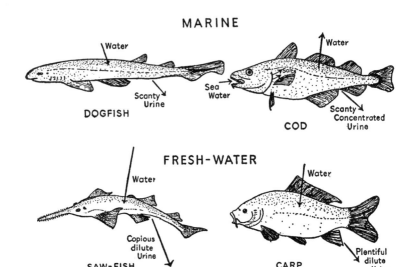

MARINE

Water

DOGFISH
Scanty
Urine

Sea
Water
Salt
COD
Scanty
Concentrated
Urine

Water

FRESH-WATER

Water

SAW-FISH
Copious
dilute
Urine

Water

CARP
Plentiful
dilute
Urine

Osmotic regulation in fishes. Explanation in the text

tion, for the osmotic pressure of the environment (sea-water) is greater than that of the fish. In consequence, water must in some way be obtained from the surrounding sea to replace that lost osmotically from the gills and the delicate lining of the mouth. These fishes therefore drink continuously, and if their gullet is blocked by inflating a small balloon in it, they soon die of thirst. The surplus salt obtained by drinking sea-water is excreted against the osmotic gradient by special chloride-secretory cells in the gill membranes. This can only be effected by the expenditure of energy. The urine, too, is very concentrated, being almost as saline as the blood.

Among fresh-water bony fishes the internal salinity of the fish is greater than that of the environment and in consequence water tends to pass into the fish across the semi-permeable membranes of the gills and buccal cavity. Surplus water is filtered from the blood by the kidney glomeruli and a copious stream of very dilute urine produced. In this respect, elasmobranchs resemble fresh-water teleosts. Urea is conserved and not excreted, and the presence of 2 per cent urea in the blood brings its total osmotic pressure above that of the sea. Consequently there is a slight osmotic gradient driving water inwards; but the urine is not quite so weak and plentiful as that of fresh-water teleosts.

Fresh-water elasmobranchs are not common, but saw-fishes, *Pristis* spp., often swim up the estuaries of Indian rivers. Here the salt content of the environment is much lower than that of their blood. In addition, some urea is retained as a legacy from their ancestors' uraemia, for their hearts cannot beat without it. In consequence the osmotic gradient driving water inwards is even greater than that of fresh-water teleosts, and the urine is very copious and dilute.

I have discussed these adaptations to life on land in some detail in order to illustrate the point that physiology and behaviour are no less complementary to one another than are morphology and behaviour. An animal is incapable of exhibiting a pattern of behaviour without the necessary structures and physiological constitution. Physiological responses are necessary for behaviour both immediately, as in the case of the hormones that engender fighting, courtship and so on, and on an evolutionary level. In fact, organisms become adapted to their environment not only immediately by their behavioural responses but slowly through the action of natural selection causing physiological and morphological changes all of which have to be taken into account.

Chapter 4

Nature by night

The unwearied sun from day to day
Does his Creator's power display,
And publishes to every land
The works of an almighty hand.
Soon as the evening shades prevail
The moon takes up the wondrous tale,
And nightly to the listening earth
Repeats the story of her birth.

JOSEPH ADDISON (1712)

THE INFLUENCE of night and day has a considerable effect upon the activities of animals and provides another example of the ways in which their behaviour is affected by their physical environment. As darkness falls, there is a drop in temperature, an increase in the relative humidity of the atmosphere and, of course, a tremendous decrease in light intensity.

Such physical changes are very marked in desert regions. Many desert animals such as centipedes, spiders, scorpions, mites, ants, beetles and other insects, snails, lizards and snakes avoid the extreme midday heat, drought and ultra-violet light by hiding under rocks and stones, or in cracks in the ground from which they emerge at dusk. Birds take refuge in the leaf-base and young shoots of palm-trees, or in bushes and camel-scrub. In the wetter parts of the tropics, on the other hand, diurnal changes in atmospheric temperature and humidity are comparatively slight.

Diurnal periodicity and behaviour

Sometimes the effects of diurnal factors are obvious. Everyone knows that the owl and badger come out at night when the hawk and squirrel have retired to rest. In other cases, however, they are more obscure. Nevertheless with the exception of animals inhabiting deep caves and the ocean bed, few creatures exist independently of the influences of nightfall and daybreak. Even among worms, those 'enliveners of wet places', we find marked twenty-four-hour rhythms of activity. Such behaviour could be in response to any of a number of physical changes, but there is reason to believe that variations in light intensity are the most widely important.

As I pointed out in the last chapter, woodlice, centipedes and millipedes lack a waterproof integument. Consequently they lose water very rapidly in dry air and cannot afford to wander in the open except at night when the atmosphere is comparatively cool and moist. Yet in most cases the factor of the environment by which their periodicity is regulated is neither temperature nor humidity, but light intensity. Although at first sight this may seem surprising, as we saw (p. 31) changes in light intensity throughout the year provide by far the most accurate and reliable indication of the onset of nightfall.

Indeed, the biological advantages to a species of rhythmic behaviour are often determined by secondary features. For example, a species may become nocturnal as an adjustment to competition from others, or to avoid being preyed upon. Thus game animals when much hunted tend to nocturnal habits, and rabbits do not come out until nightfall in areas where much shooting occurs. Conversely, predators must be nocturnal if their prey comes out only at night.

The nocturnal habit confers many advantages. Enemies are more easily avoided and food more easily obtained than during the day. Losses of moisture are reduced because the air at night is more nearly saturated, and intercommunication between members of the same species is facilitated because odours are more readily conveyed. The carnivorous habit is less hazardous too at night, and competition is reduced when nocturnal carnivores such as beetles prey on sleeping diurnal forms such as butterflies.

Not only are many factors involved, but these may mutually influence one another. For example, whilst some nocturnal animals are never active in the daytime, others can alter their habits in different circumstances. Thus the African buffalo was very abundant until, in 1890, a terrible epidemic of rinderpest almost exterminated them in many places. Whereas previously the animals used to feed in herds in the open by day, the survivors retired to forests and dense swamps, feeding only at night. After a number of years, however, buffaloes increased considerably and returned to their former diurnal behaviour.

Some animals are active during a certain period of the day or night, others exhibit different kinds of activity at different times. Many normally diurnal birds migrate at night and aquatic insects which spend the daytime swimming about in ponds and streams usually fly from one locality to another during the hours of darkness. An interesting example of the periodic movement of animals is recorded from a small island off the coast of Ceylon. This is inhabited at night by crows which roost in the trees. In the morning

A flying-fox

they fly to the mainland to feed and their place is taken by fruit-eating bats or 'flying-foxes' which fly to the island at dawn.

Truly social animals are seldom nocturnal, but nocturnal species may form aggregations for feeding or hibernation. At the same time nocturnal forms are frequently primitive and may have long fossil records. So there may be an evolutionary aspect to the problem of nocturnalism, but studies of the physiology of vertebrate eyes which may become adapted to diurnal or nocturnal vision suggest that diurnality and nocturnality come and go as mutation and ecological expedients direct. Thus the physiological and ecological aspects of behaviour in relation to day and night are closely inter-related.

Rhythms in insects

The acquisition of a diurnal rhythm of activity is illustrated by the Congo floor-maggot which is the larva of an African blowfly, *Auchmeromyia luteola*. The adult is a shade-loving insect which frequents human habitations where it feeds on fallen fruit, fermenting garbage, excrement and so on. The eggs are usually laid in the dust in cracks of floors of huts and under the sleeping mats of the African natives where the larvae conceal themselves during the

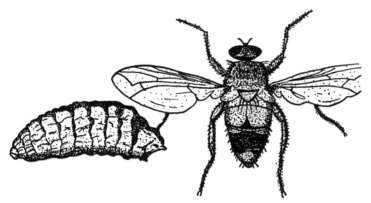

The Congo floor-maggot and adult fly

day. At night, however, when the inhabitants lie asleep on their mats, these maggots crawl up and suck their blood.

The bite is apparently not painful, the Africans do not seem to mind it and there are no pathological complications. The periodicity of these insects is correlated with a response to temperature. At night they are attracted to the warmth of human bodies, but after feeding the response becomes negative. The rhythm, which can easily be reversed experimentally, is acquired in the course of larval existence and is regulated by the habits of the Africans who return to their houses to sleep at sunset. Once it has been acquired however, the rhythm will persist under constant conditions for several days.

A somewhat different rhythm is seen in the moulting of insects, the hatching of their eggs and emergence of pupae. These proceedings usually occur at a definite time of day and will continue to do so for several generations under constant conditions, again indicating the presence of an internal 'clock' system. The study of aphids has shown that there is a diurnal periodicity of flight and nocturnal quiescence which is reflected at heights of up to 2,000 feet above ground level. Moonlight too has a considerable influence on the activity of insects at night. For instance, the number of noctuid moths attracted to light traps is much reduced on nights of full moon, and there is a difference between the hours of flight of these Lepidoptera, according to whether the early or late portion of the night is moonlit.

From work of this kind we know that the majority of insects, as of other animals, possess a periodicity which responds to the alternation of day and night. Most Hymenoptera, including bees and wasps, are diurnal, as are predatory insects such as robber-flies, many tiger-beetles, scorpion-flies and dragon-flies, while stag-beetles, chafers, termites, mosquitoes, bed bugs, cockroaches, weevils and many caterpillars are nocturnal. At first sight it may seem strange that insects which shun the daylight should be strongly attracted to artificial lights at night, but orientation responses may vary both with the strength of the stimulus and the physiological state of the recipient. It has been found, however, that attack by codling moth is reduced if apple trees are illuminated at night, because oviposition is inhibited by light in this species.

Disease and the biting cycles of mosquitoes

The possibility that the nocturnal activity of mosquitoes may also be influenced by moonlight has received considerable attention in recent years, but the question seems to be a very complicated one. A knowledge of the biting cycles of mosquitoes may have considerable economic and medical importance, particularly in respect to the epidemiology of malaria and yellow fever. For example, some species of *Anopheles* bite mostly at dusk, others in the middle of the night, others at dawn. Yet in many hospitals in Africa, mosquito nets are raised when the patients are awakened before sunrise. The inmates must therefore run an unnecessary risk of contracting infection. Troops are ordered to wear anti-mosquito clothing at dusk, yet are paraded unprotected in the morning, just when the biting cycle of some species of mosquito reaches its peak.

Most experiments have been made by counting the number of mosquitoes attracted to human 'bait' and striking results have been obtained concerning biting activity in relation to vertical distribution. Although there is a sharp fall in biting activity with increase in height above the ground, the amount of feeding at ground level may vary considerably. It is evidently influenced by local conditions such as the presence of thick bush around camps and villages. In addition, low temperatures inhibit biting even at dusk, and the peak activity of crepuscular (twilight-active) species appears to be controlled by the light intensity at sunset.

Malarial parasites are probably particularly numerous in the blood system at the peak times of the biting activity of mosquitoes that harbour them.

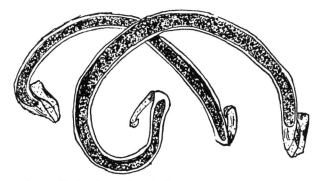

Microfilaria of *Wuchereria bancrofti*, the cause of elephantiasis (greatly enlarged)

Another periodicity which is important in medicine is that shown by microfilaria larvae of *Wuchereria bancrofti*, the organism responsible for the terrible disease of elephantiasis. The adults of this nematode worm inhabit the lymphatic vessels of man, whereas the microfilariae remain in the blood stream. They are rarely found in the blood stream during the day, but towards evening appear in increasing numbers. By midnight there may be as many as 40 or 50 millions in the circulatory system of the patient. Their number decreases during the latter part of the night, and by 9 o'clock in the morning they have again disappeared from the peripheral blood. This diurnal periodicity may be maintained with the utmost regularity for ten or more years. If the filarial patient is made to sleep during the day and remain awake at night, the rhythm of the microfilariae becomes reversed in 3 or 4 days. The presence of the parasites in the blood stream is not a direct response to the sleepy state of the host, because they begin to appear several hours before the usual time of sleep, and do not disappear until after the usual time of waking. Filarial periodicity has yet to be satisfactorily explained. It is obviously an adaptation to the biting cycle of the mosquito *Culex fatigans*, the intermediate host of the parasite. It cannot be that the movement of microfilariae through the cutaneous blood vessels is obstructed least when the body is fatigued — as some authors have supposed — because some varieties of *W. bancrofti* are non-periodic, and others show a reversed periodicity where the intermediate host is a day-biting mosquito. It has been suggested that during the active phase of their rhythm, the microfilariae move into the capillaries of the lung whence they are distributed throughout the blood-system during the passive phase. Probably periodicity is a quality inherent in the microfilariae themselves.

I believe that probably all living cells possess an inherent twenty-four-hour rhythmicity normally synchronised with diurnal environmental changes. It is possible in some cases to alter experimentally the time of activity of an organism without affecting the synchronisation of its rhythm, just as one might shift the dial of a clock without altering the position of the hands.

Sense organs

In strictly nocturnal or diurnal species there is usually a refinement of one or more of the senses and differences are of degree rather than of kind. Scent is perhaps most important at night for the congregation of individuals, sex attraction, following the tracks of prey, location of enemies and so on; hearing and sound-production for communication, the detection of enemies or victims; light production for sex attraction and warning. Diurnal periodicity in sound production at dusk and dawn has been studied in the tropical rain-forest fauna of an island in the Panama Canal Zone. In this investigation there was found to be a correlation between sound-production by diurnal and nocturnal animals (cicadas,* grasshoppers and crickets, frogs, birds and monkeys) and the physical influences, such as daylight, operating on them.

The sensitive elements in the retina of the vertebrate eye are of two kinds: rods and cones. Animals that are adapted for night

---

* Only male cicadas sing: females do not possess sound-producing organs. That is why the Greek satirical poet Xenarchus (fourth century B.C.), evidently a married man, wrote: 'Happy the Cicadas' lives, for they all have voiceless wives.'

vision have a particularly large number of rods. In man, the central part of the retina, the *fovea centralis* or 'yellow spot' on which objects are normally focused, consists almost entirely of cones. These

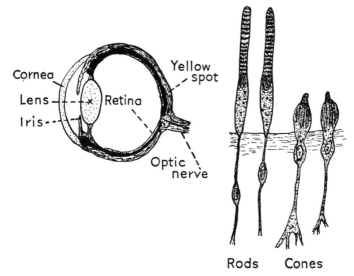

Left, diagram of the eye; *right*, rods and cones of the retina (greatly enlarged)

are responsible for colour-vision and for detailed resolution. Towards the periphery of the retina the proportion of rods increases. That is why a very faint star can often be seen only when one looks slightly to one side of it, a principle frequently employed by astronomers. Colour-blindness in nocturnal animals such as mice is associated with lack of cones.

In the eyes of nocturnal animals a reflecting mechanism or *'tapetum'* is usually present. Any light passing through the retina is reflected back so that there is a double chance for a given ray to stimulate a rod. The absence of a tapetum in owls illustrates the super efficiency of the retinal rods through which little or no light passes. There are many kinds of tapetum, but reflection is most frequently caused by fibrous tissue or guanine crystals. Associated with a very efficient retina as in the opossum, a tapetum results in such sensitivity that bright light is avoided at all times, even though a slit pupil very greatly reduces the amount of light penetrating to the retina, and ensures some protection by means of its fine control.

The larger terrestrial mammals — buffaloes, elephants, lions, bears and so on — have eyes which are not particularly specialised either for day or night vision. They have a tapetum and sufficient rods for reasonable visual sensitivity, and yet have many cones also. These, coupled with a large eyeball, ensure good resolution of detail. In consequence, vision is relatively good both at night and by day, even where senses of smell and hearing are acute, and the animals are not very markedly nocturnal or diurnal.

There is an Arabian fable concerning an argument between the horse and the lion as to which had the keener sight. The lion could distinguish a white pearl in milk on a dark night, but the horse could see a black pearl in a heap of coal in the day. The matter was submitted to arbitration and the judges rightly pronounced in favour of the horse. No doubt they realised that the acuity of the cone vision of the Perissodactyla is greater than that of the nocturnal rods and tapetum of the Carnivora.

Nocturnal forms often have an iris with a vertical pupil aperture, and adaptations may also occur in the lens. For example, flying squirrels, *Glaucomys* spp., are nocturnal and have colourless lenses, whereas true squirrels, *Sciurus* spp., are diurnal and have yellow lenses. Both types inhabit the same forests in many localities, and their different periods of activity are related to the light-filtering properties of their eyes.

In diurnal eyes, intra-ocular oil droplets act in the same way as filters in photography. The red droplets in birds are effective at sunrise, but as the day wears on, the yellow and colourless droplets are most effective: at sunset the red oil droplets again come into operation. Thus late-rising birds such as hawks have fewer red droplets than song birds. Red droplets enable turtles to see through the surface glare of a tropical sea.

Yellow filters cut out much of the violet light, and some blue. These are the colours responsible for most chromatic aberration. At the same time they enhance contrast, and do not impede natural hues. A combination of a yellow diurnal lens or yellow droplets with a tapetum would result in poor vision at all times, and does not occur in nature.

Of the six or eight eyes possessed by the majority of spiders, some are black, others pearly-white. They were at one time described as diurnal and nocturnal respectively and it was believed that one type was used in the daytime, the other at night. The evidence for this is, however, slight. The chief visual organs of insects and crustaceans are the compound eyes, made up of a number of transparent facets each with an elongated, light-sensitive structure beneath it. In diurnal insects images are formed by *apposition* — that is, the light passing through each facet falls only on the appropriate optic-rod or *'rhabdom'*. In many nocturnal insects such as noctuid moths, glow-worm beetles and the like, there is a special kind of compound eye that forms images by *superposition*. Each sensory rhabdom receives light rays not only through its own facet, but through neighbouring facets also. Between these two extremes there are many intermediate stages. Light and dark adaptation of compound eyes is achieved by migration of the pigment in each optical unit or *'ommatidium'*, so that the rhabdom is more or less shielded. Similarly migration of rods, cones and retinal pigment is of great importance in the lower vertebrates.

In many species, therefore, there is a marked specialisation for a nocturnal or diurnal habit. Diurnal animals have become adapted to meet, or to avoid, relatively high temperatures and evaporation rates, bright light and decreased conductivity of the air for odours. Conversely, nocturnal species are adapted to decreased temperatures, high humidity, dim light and increased conductivity of the air for odours. It has been suggested that crepuscular species may be confined to the short periods of dusk or dawn, simply because they are relatively unspecialised in these respects; but this cannot apply to the hawk-moths which are highly adapted to activity in twilight.

Degree of specialisation in man

The question arises, how persistent are twenty-four-hour rhythms of activity? Some species respond directly to physical changes in the environment, others show periodicities which persist under constant conditions. Some show rigid behaviour patterns while others, like the buffaloes already cited, are able to reverse their habits. In man the degree of specialisation to a nocturnal or diurnal existence is not particularly marked. That men are essentially diurnal is indicated, I think, by the terrors that darkness may hold for young children. There can be few adults either who do not feel a quickening of the pulse when they are out alone at night. Yet I well remember, that whilst escaping after losing my tank in the disastrous battle of Villers Bocage, I welcomed the nightfall that allowed me to leave my daytime hiding places and never felt the slightest bit nervous after dark.

Like most young animals, the human baby is non-rhythmic

during its first year of life, as parents are only too well aware, but gradually there is an increasing range and regularity of the twenty-four-hour physiological rhythms of body temperature, urine secretion and so on, as the child becomes progressively adapted to a normal rhythmic existence. Although as individuals we are markedly periodic and those who have to work night shifts take a long time to become adjusted, nevertheless social communities as a whole are less periodic the larger they are. Thus the isolated family or hamlet may be completely rhythmic, but in a small town there is usually someone awake at night, if only the policeman. In larger cities there is a considerable degree of night life. An interesting parallel is afforded by ants and some other social animals. In man it may take some while before the normal metabolic curve with its daytime peak is reversed and when the members of the Vienna Philharmonic Orchestra flew to Tokyo, it was several days before they all became acclimatised to the new times. It has been suggested therefore, that greater individual and communal efficiency might result if night shifts were lengthened to consecutive periods oı several weeks or months, so that the rhythm might have time to become completely reversed. Of course, means of recreation and other facilities would have to be available at night too, for the scheme to work.

Experiments carried out on people living within the Arctic circle in summer when the sun never sets below the horizon, have disclosed considerable individual variation in the ability of the human body to become adapted to rhythms of frequency other than twenty-four-hours. It has been known for a long time that there is some relation between heart rate and body temperature in man — indeed in pre-thermometer days, physicians often judged the degree of fever by the rapidity of the pulse. More recently it has been found that diurnal fluctuations of heart rate and body temperature are correlated and that thyroid medication raises both of these variables together. Also, a shift in, or inversion of the diurnal body temperature range is accompanied by a similar change in heart rate variation.

In one experiment, twelve human subjects lived as two isolated communities in Spitzbergen (79° N, 16° E) for seven weeks. External environmental conditions showed little variation in either light or temperature so that it was possible to impose abnormal time routines without this becoming apparent. Specially adjusted twenty-one-hour and twenty-seven-hour wrist watches were worn

PLATE V

Whitethroat
removing
white
faecal sac
of young

PLATE VI

American belted
kingfisher and prey

PLATE VII

Giant water-bug feeding on leopard frog

PLATE VIII

Male Pacific
rattlesnakes
fighting

so that the subjects of the experiment would always live on the experimental time routines.

The rhythm of body temperature became adapted almost immediately to the abnormal time routines in eleven of the twelve subjects, in marked contrast to the excretory rhythms which adapted immediately in only three. Analysis of the data obtained, confirmed that when living on a normal twenty-four-hour routine, the excretory rhythms for water, chloride and potassium were extremely similar, both in amplitude and timing. On the abnormal routines, however, small but statistically significant differences between the three rhythms were very common and marked dissociations not uncommon.

The usual type of marked dissociation was that in which the rhythm of potassium excretion was out of phase with those of chloride and water, the potassium excretory rhythm showing more evidence of the persistence of an inherent twenty-four-hour component. Examples of marked dissociation between the excretory rhythms of water and chloride were rare. Thus, of the four rhythms studied, that of body temperature appeared to be the most determined by the environment, that of potassium excretion the most determined by the intrinsic mechanism with a twenty-four-hour periodicity.

It is therefore clearly impossible to assume that all diurnal rhythms in man are controlled by a single mechanism: at least two mechanisms must be involved to produce the observed independence of response. Inherent twenty-four-hour excretory periodicities were persistent in many of the subjects, while the sleep rhythm showed rapid adaptation to abnormal routines in almost all subjects. Nevertheless, the ratio of sleep/wakefulness appears to be constant for individual subjects, regardless of the time occupied by the complete daily routine, and it is not unlikely that sleep rhythms may affect the rhythm of body temperature which adapts equally rapidly in most subjects.

Sleep

The physiological necessity of sleep to animals is familiar if unexplained and it is natural that the alternation of periods of activity with repose should be correlated with the physical conditions of day and night. Sleep is a true instinct in mammals, controlled by the hypothalamus, which is the brain centre for all instinctive behaviour.

Little is known of the sleeping habits of wild animals. Many species sleep in characteristic poses which we seldom see because the creatures are easily disturbed and react by flight. For example, crayfish and snakes assume rigid and bizarre postures.

Fishes often sleep on the bottom of a pond or stream; birds tuck their heads under their wings and bats hang upside down.

Sleeping position of the potto

Whales, sea-lions and some seals sleep under water, only coming to the surface to breathe. Many small mammals such as the dormouse, potto and some sloths sleep curled up in a ball, while the fox uses his bushy tail as a pillow. Elephants sleep only for a couple of hours about midnight. A healthy elephant may lie with its trunk coiled up like a rope and its head resting on a pillow of vegetation. Elephants that are sick or upset, however, do not lie down at all, but merely doze for short periods whilst standing up. Giraffe too, only sleep for a few hours: they hold their heads erect, occasionally and for brief intervals resting their heads on the ground or on their backs.

The most striking manifestation of sleep is the partial or complete depression of the higher nervous centres, a state which is subjectively described as unconsciousness. It is only animals that stand on a comparatively high level of mental development which show sleep comparable to that of man, for it is only the higher parts of the central nervous system that are involved. As a result of muscular relaxation, metabolism is reduced, the temperature drops and respiration becomes slower and deeper. The rate of heart beat decreases and the concentration of carbon dioxide in the blood becomes greater. At the same time, digestive processes proceed in a normal manner and all kinds of stimuli are capable of producing physiological effects on the sleeper without waking him.

It has been suggested that sleep represents a state of inhibition always present in some areas of the brain, but which has now become diffused throughout the entire cortex even descending to some of the lower parts. The details of experimental results are in agreement with this interpretation. For example, prolonged stimulation of the same region of the cortex results in mental depression and lethargy, whilst a great number of quickly changing stimuli tend to keep an animal alert. However, there is no sharp dividing line between sleep and wakefulness, and the state of alertness is probably only an expression of a preponderance of excitation.

Since the time of Lucretius* it has been believed that sleeping dogs may dream. A dog will make chewing movements with its jaws if food is placed before it whilst it is sleeping. A veteran horse who served in the Turko-Italian war, in later life would neigh excitedly in its sleep and kick with its hooves as though living again the scenes of battle. Sleeping chimpanzees sometimes indulge in wild howling and it has been suggested that this may be caused by nightmares. But the proof of subjective phenomena such as dreams in animals must ever remain beyond our grasp.

* Titus Carus (c. 98–55 B.C.), *De Rerum Naturae* Lib. IV: 'In truth you will see strong horses, when their limbs are lain to rest, yet sweat in their sleep, and pant for ever, and strain every nerve as though for victory. . . . And hunters' dogs often in their soft sleep yet suddenly toss their legs, and all at once give tongue, and again and again snuff the air with their nostrils, as if they had found and were following the tracks of wild beasts.' Trans. C. Bailey, Oxford, 1947.

53

Chapter 5

The language of animals

So far we have been considering behaviour in response to physical factors of the environment. In discussing the ways in which animals communicate, we enter the field of behaviour that is concerned with the interactions of individuals and of groups of animals. In nature the two are superimposed.

The language of animals, unlike our own, does not need to be learned, for it consists of innate signals. Man may involuntarily indicate his feelings or emotions by laughing, yawning, crying and so on, but because he is accustomed to relying upon the language of words, his ability to interpret instinctive expressions is by no means as acute as it might be.

We know that dogs express 'pleasure' by tail-wagging, 'anger' by growling, 'fear' by whining and so on. (I have used the subjective terms 'pleasure', 'anger' and 'fear' as a convenient shorthand for accurate, but more lengthy objective terminology.) Detailed study has shown that, in fact, animals have a far more extensive and complicated sign language than may be apparent on cursory inspection. Wolves, like dogs, have a variety of postures and behaviour patterns which stimulate others of their kind.

The language of animals is nevertheless almost entirely a 'mood indicator'. It is a method by which an animal conveys its social status and intentions, friendly or otherwise, towards another member of the species. It is used to co-ordinate the activities of the family or group, to give warning of danger, notification of established territory and so on. This language consists of 'signs' to which other animals respond, in much the same way as they react in their maintenance activities to simple sign stimuli provided by the physical environment, enemies or food. Attempts to raise chimpanzees like human children, completely away from their kind, have never resulted in the animals learning to talk human

54

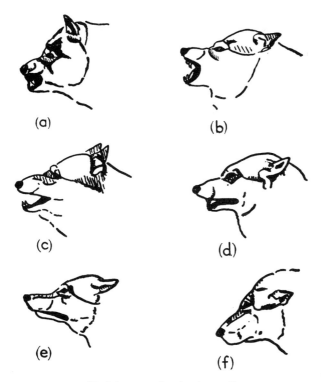

Facial expression in the wolf

(*a*) Threat, high intensity, no uncertainty.
(*b*) High intensity, slight uncertainty.
(*c*) Threat, low intensity with uncertainty.
(*d*) Weak threat with strong uncertainty.
(*e*) Anxiety.
(*f*) Uncertainty with suspicion in the face of an enemy.

These figures show how many expressive emotional attitudes must have survived domestication to appear unchanged in domestic dogs

language even though the brain and motor apparatus of the chimpanzee is similar to that of man.

Releaser phenomena

A tick bites when it receives a combination of two stimuli, the smell of butyric acid and a temperature of 37° C. Blue tits feed the gaping yellow beaks of their young and remove the white excretory sacs from their nest. A jackdaw attacks a man carrying a black

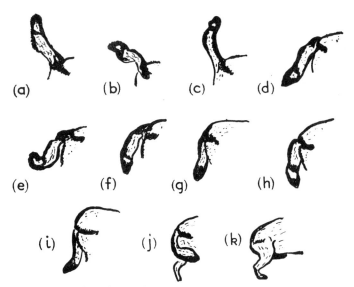

Use of the tail for expression in the wolf

(*a*) Self-confidence in social group.
(*b*) Confident threat.
(*c*) With wagging; imposing carriage.
(*d*) Normal carriage (in a situation without social tension).
(*e*) Somewhat uncertain threat.
(*f*) Similar to (*d*) but specially common in feeding and guarding.
(*g*) Depressed mood.
(*h*) Intermediate between threat and defence.
(*i*) Active submission (with wagging).
(*j*) and (*k*) Complete submission.

bathing dress. All these instinctive acts are elicited in response to particular sign stimuli known as '*releasers*'.

Butyric acid is a normal constituent of sweat but it is most unlikely that a combination of this chemical with blood heat would occur naturally anywhere except on the body of a mammal. Therefore, although the stimuli that induce the biting reaction of a tick are relatively simple, it is most improbable that the creature would encounter them both together except on the body of its host. The same characteristics, simplicity and improbability, are found in the sign stimuli that release the feeding response of a mother tit. The instinct to rescue another member of the species who has been captured by a predatory mammal, is released in jackdaws by the sight of a black object being carried. In the example given above, however, the jackdaw's behaviour pattern was released fortuitously and in quite inappropriate circumstances, and therefore clearly illustrates the automatic nature of the reaction.

Ordered phenomena tend to be rare in nature, disorderly mixtures more probable. Hence releasers usually take the form of pure spectral colours, pure song notes and so on. The appropriate behaviour patterns are not likely to be released inadvertently and in the wrong situation unless some experimenter deliberately fools the animal with an artificial releaser!

Display of the fiddler-crab

Few releasers operate unless accompanied by an instinctive act of display on the part of their bearer, but the releasers which elicit the pursuit reaction of social species are automatic. Examples are afforded by the white tails of rabbits and the brightly coloured wing feathers of ducks, which cannot be seen unless the birds are flying.

It is not by chance that similar jigging movements, which are both striking and simple, have been evolved as releasers independently in parrots, gulls, spoonbills and other unrelated groups of birds. On the other hand, related species often show markedly different forms of display. For example, fiddler-crabs of species that can be separated in the laboratory only with considerable difficulty and the aid of the microscope are readily distinguishable in the field by their different behaviour patterns and the ways in which the males signal with their enlarged claws during courtship.

That releasers are not dependent solely upon structure or colour is shown by cases in which the same character has various uses. Thus the raven uses its plumage differently in courtship and threat. Indeed, it is probable that in most cases the releaser ceremony may be older than the structures and colours associated with it. The peacock and pheasant must obviously have acquired the habit of displaying their tail to their mates before conspicuous

Peacock in display

colours were acquired as a result of selection. Although there is no evidence that female birds actually choose the most brightly coloured male, nevertheless the more striking individuals are no doubt particularly effective in stimulating mating responses.

At the same time, in addition to its physiological functions, sexual dimorphism may serve to draw the attention of predatory enemies to the more conspicuous and less valuable sex; for males and females do not bear the same relationship to the environment as regards escape from enemies. Thus a passing hawk is more likely to carry off a brightly coloured drake or cock pheasant than his sombrely coloured mate who will be left to incubate her brood. On the other hand, sexual dimorphism does not occur in larger and

58

more formidable species, nor in those in which both sexes share in the task of incubation.

It is, perhaps, not surprising that emergency and distress signals should tend to be somewhat similar in different species. Consequently a mother mallard will respond to the piping of a muscovy duckling and fly to its defence. But if it should then join her own brood she will treat it as a stranger and kill it.

An illustration of the extent of the response of birds to an alarm call is afforded by the work of an American professor who recorded the distress shriek of a starling. He then toured the roosts of a small town much infested by starlings in an amplifying car with the volume turned up as high as possible. The effect on the human inhabitants was not described, but the starlings left for good! Animals do not always respond identically, however, to the same stimulus and personal acquaintance may dominate instinctive releaser actions. Thus yet another variable factor is introduced into the simplest reflex system by which a certain stimulus invariably results in the same response.

An interesting example is afforded by the effect of learning on the behaviour of fishes. At one time visitors to the Aquarium of the London Zoo were surprised to see a shoal of small roach sharing a tank with a giant twenty-pound pike. The roach had been introduced one by one, as food for the pike; but when the latter was not in the mood for dining, after a few hours it apparently presented them with 'the freedom of the tank'. From then onwards, even if the pike were hungry it would not molest them. When seemingly identical roach were introduced with the 'untouchables' they would at once be seized with unerring aim, none of the older inhabitants ever being engulfed by mistake, although they appeared to present identical releaser stimuli.

It would be rash to suggest that the pike harboured any finer feelings towards its small companions or even that it derived satisfaction from their proximity. Its compassionate behaviour is not therefore easily explained.

On another occasion a pike was separated by a sheet of glass from some small fish sharing its tank. In this instance, however, it was the violent contact with the glass whenever it made an attack that apparently impressed the pike. For when the glass was at last removed the small fish were left severely alone although any stranger was greedily devoured as soon as it was introduced.

A somewhat analogous case has been reported from the Amster-

Threat display of male sticklebacks

dam aquarium. On one occasion the tanks were stocked to capacity when the authorities, unexpectedly acquiring a shoal of mullet, were in a dilemma as to where to accommodate them. It was finally decided to accommodate them with the turtles and the fish were introduced with considerable uproar and disturbance of the water.

This ruse was adopted because it was feared that the turtles, accustomed to eating dead fish, might regard the living article as a pleasant addition to their diet. As intended, the reptiles apparently associated the fish with the cataclysmic breaking of their accustomed peace, and left them severely alone. A few months later some more mullet arrived. On the assumption that they would share the immunity of their predecessors, they were added to the tank's population, only to be singled out and devoured by the turtles. As it was feared that the turtles' appetites might in time outweigh their awe of the original mullet, these fishes were given a tank to themselves as soon as circumstances permitted.

The effect upon the turtles was startling. They began to mope, refused food and showed every sign of dejection. As a last resource whereby to awaken their interest in life, the original fish were reintroduced. At once the turtles recovered their appetites and customary liveliness!

Imprinting

Releasers are often affected by *'imprinting'*. This is a special type of learning, found mostly in birds and insects, which takes place very quickly and is almost irreversible. An example is afforded by the pathetic case of the grasshopper who, at an early age, was taught the wrong song. Thereafter, females of his own species ignored his supplications, so he was doomed to a life of continual frustration!

Imprinting often takes place long before the reaction itself is established. Consequently the individual from whom the stimulus issues in the first place does not necessarily function as an object of the reaction in later life. Hand-reared owls and ravens may never breed, because they respond sexually to their keepers instead of to members of their own species. A case is known of a gander who persistently courted a wooden kennel in which he was reared! But normally young birds become imprinted on their parents and from then on are able to recognise and respond to members of their own species although obviously this process cannot apply in the case of cuckoos.

Intercommunication

The language of animals consists of signs which may be optic, acoustic, tactile, olfactory or various combinations of these. Thus the fiddler-crab waves his claw at a trespasser, one male stickleback

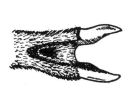 

Olfactory glands in ruminants. Left, pedal gland of the muntjac; right, pre-orbital gland of the male four-horned antelope

threatens another by adopting a vertical, head-down position and the giraffe is said to show his whole body against the sky-line.

Male grasshoppers chirrup, frogs croak, alligators and stags roar. In this way they indicate that they have established a 'territory'. If one howler monkey group enters the territory of another a vocal battle ensues between the respective males supported by the whines of their females and young. This continues until one, generally the 'home team', wins. There is usually no fighting.

Male antelope marking a tree with the secretion from a scent gland near the eye

Most mammals except seals, monkeys and man have a strong sense of smell. Not infrequently scents are used to demark territory. In some cases special scent glands have been evolved for this purpose, like those beside the eyes of antelopes: in others, excrement or urine are used. This explains why a dog may lift his leg at almost every lamp post but a bitch shows more restraint! Upkeep of scent marks is the prerogative of the male who has to defend his territory: female animals are usually without scent glands.

Courtship, the subject of a later chapter, is a form of intercommunication which has an important function in synchronising mating activities. For not only does it serve to bring the sexes together, but it ensures that mating takes place when both partners are in a state of physiological readiness. It also prevents hybridisation between related species which, as we have seen, often possess quite distinctive patterns of display which act as releasers. Finally, communication is necessary to keep together the members of social species. Wolves and jackals hunt within hearing of one another so that the pack is not dispersed in close country. Migrating birds react by sight and sound; shoaling fishes by sight, sound or smell. Indeed, visual, auditory and olfactory stimuli, singly or in various combinations, are all employed in intercommunication.

Animals of different species are really never able to make friends with one another because their different languages are instinctive and cannot be learned. Nevertheless they may misunderstand each other at times. A tame condor in the Amsterdam zoo hopped over to greet the director with outstretched wings. At this, a vulture in a nearby cage turned in the same direction and spread his wings, looked 'puzzled', clapped his wings together and walked off. Possibly he thought that the condor was sunning itself and then realised that the sun was not shining! A stag and a large kangaroo were placed in the same enclosure. All went well as long as the kangaroo sat on all fours, but whenever it rose to its typical bipedal stance, the stag attacked it. To rear on one's hind legs is an invitation to battle in the language of stags, and the response was inevitable.

Animals *stare* at one another only when they intend to attack, or are afraid. Hence they do not 'like' being stared at. Peripheral vision is more efficient in most mammals than it is in man, but they do not obtain such a clear image. So if one wishes to 'make friends' with an animal, it is advisable not to look fixedly at it.

Domesticated animals often become adept at interpreting their owner's thoughts. Dogs soon know if they are to be taken for a walk or left at home; indeed, they sometimes seem to have an uncanny knowledge of what a person is planning. This is based, not on an understanding of human language, but on observation of the innumerable signs, both voluntary and involuntary, which indicate a person's intention or mood.

Horses as well as dogs have been known which seemed to be capable of quite complex mathematical calculations. In every case, however, experiment has shown that the owner or trainer, voluntarily or involuntarily, gave the solution to the animal. For when he himself did not know the right answer, his unfortunate animal continued to knock or bark, waiting in vain for the sign that would tell him to stop when the requisite number had been reached.

Few people, even with the utmost self-control, can withhold an unconscious, involuntary signal. So in research work on animal psychology it is important to ensure that the experimenter cannot be seen by the experimental animal, otherwise mistaken conclusions may be reached.

It is often said that human beings are unique in possessing a well-developed verbal language and to a certain extent this is true. From the above paragraphs, however, it will be seen that many animals possess in rudimentary form the basic characteristics of human language. Vocal communication occurs also in insects, fishes, amphibians, reptiles, birds and mammals. The human speaker conveys as much of his emotional state by his tone as by his actual words — animal language consists almost entirely of conveying moods and emotions. Nevertheless, communication amongst social insects (p. 116) results in the transference of information about objects and events apart from the organism passing the information. Human language can be used as an instrument to produce effects on other animals — so can the bark of a dog asking to be let out!

Human speech can be used as a system of symbols for solving problems and in this it may be unique, for there is no evidence of similar processes amongst other species. On the other hand, chimpanzees, dogs and other mammals can solve problems of such complexity that some process analogous to visualisation must be involved. Indeed, the only characteristic of human language which appears to be unique is the fact that it is learned largely independently of heredity, yet even here the evolution and spread of different vowel sounds has been traced across Europe.

We must, therefore, conclude that human language and, in fact, all human thought must have evolved from capabilities present among other species. The chief differences lie not so much qualitatively as in the degree to which they are exploited.

Chapter 6

Feeding and fighting

Territory

WITHIN ITS GEOGRAPHICAL RANGE, every species has its own particular habitat or '*biochore*'. Thus a forest dweller such as the squirrel is found only in wooded districts, the otter lives near water and the brown rat near human dwellings. This aspect of behaviour is extremely important in ecology.

During the Middle Ages, the Black Death killed more than half the population of Europe and the disease was still a menace to life until the end of the seventeenth century, after which it practically disappeared in the West. As we now know, plague is carried by rats from which the bacilli are transmitted to human beings by rat fleas and its disappearance was partly due to improvements in the conditions under which people were living. But this was not the only reason. At the time when plague was still a serious menace to life, the common species of rat in Europe was *Rattus rattus*, the black or ship rat. This animal is a very effective plague carrier owing to its habit of living in houses in rather close contact with man. In 1727, however, great hordes of another species, the brown rat, *R. norvegicus*, were seen in Russia marching westwards and swimming across the Volga near Astrakhan. Later the whole continent of Europe was occupied by them and the original black rats were, to a large extent driven out. Nowadays black rats are found chiefly on ships and in ports. The brown rat tends to live in sewers and outhouses and its habits do not bring it into such close contact with man. Consequently, since that time, plague has ceased to be a serious epidemic disease in Europe.

Within its habitat a species may be restricted to an ecological niche or '*biotope*' in which it makes its home: it is not free to roam anywhere within its geographical range. For this reason, animals in captivity are not necessarily restricted psychologically, for even in the wild they do not wander at random.

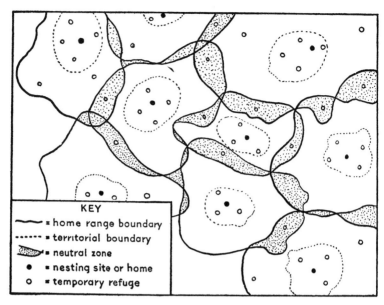

KEY

— = home range boundary
----- = territorial boundary
▨ = neutral zone
● = nesting site or home
○ = temporary refuge

Diagrammatic representation of the accepted concepts
of territory and home range

The smallest subdivision of the biotope of an animal is its
'*territory*'. This can be defined as 'any defended area'. Territories
are clearly indicated by their owners who mark them with various
signs (see p. 62). These may be optic, olfactory and auditory, used
singly or in various combinations. For example, the blackbird or
robin clearly demarks his territory by singing in a conspicuous
position. His song is not a paean of joy, but a threat or warning to
intruders. The alligator marks its territory by acoustic and olfactory
signs, the brown bear by olfactory and optic signals.

The size of the territory varies considerably in different species.
That of the hawk may be as large as the bird's total living space,
but those of blackbirds include only the nest and display areas with
neutral zones in between.

Furthermore, not all the available space within a territory is
utilised. As all hunters know, most animals follow special tracks
within their territories and flightless birds such as ostriches and
penguins, use regular beats. Even strong fliers such as vultures and
birds of prey keep to certain areas of their territories for soaring.
The hippopotamus has a pear-shaped territory and spends his days
wallowing in the water at the 'stalk' end.

66

Within its territory an animal such as a fox or badger may have, in addition to its home, various refuges or temporary earths which are often closely linked by pathways and graded in use and importance. The home is generally surrounded by a protected area in

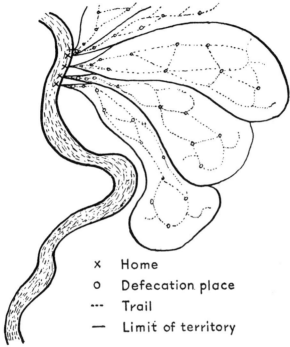

x Home
o Defecation place
... Trail
— Limit of territory

Diagram of several pear-shaped hippopotamus territories furrowed with trails and landmarked with places for defecation. In its aquatic home this animal mates, gives birth, nurses its young and, in the case of danger, takes refuge in the water

which prey is not hunted. Thus pigeons may nest with impunity beside a hawk's eyrie, and roe deer are safe by the wolf's den.

This 'cease-fire' area is probably a protective device which automatically prevents parent animals from attacking their own offspring. In the case of herbivores, the vegetation near the home may often be so strongly impregnated with body scents that it has lost its attraction as food and the animals always browse in another part of the territory.

Predatory animals tend to keep certain areas of their territory

67

for dismembering the prey, others are reserved for drinking, bathing, wallowing, defecating, urinating, depositing scent marks or as larders, rubbing places, play areas and so on. All these parts of the territory are connected by well-known paths and often visited at the same time each day.

Human beings, too, appear to have a genuine territorial instinct. Refugee children housed in large spacious rooms soon showed symptoms of psychological deficiency. But when the rooms were split into separate compartments in which the children felt 'at home', their symptoms disappeared. Prisoners of war often develop a peculiarly possessive attitude to the small space allocated to them, and everyone knows the annoyance of having one's privacy invaded.

Male European bison 'marking' a tree by barking a portion of the trunk with its horns. After this the animal will urinate, roll in its urine and then rub its back against the tree trunk

Feeding habits

Where closely related species inhabit the same biochore they usually exploit different sources of food. For example, the shag feeds mostly on free-swimming fishes whilst the cormorant eats flat-fish, shrimps, prawns and small crabs. In the case of many hawks the two sexes differ considerably in size and do not compete for food. In the same way, as we have seen (p. 12), large spiders eat large insects while smaller species are attracted to smaller prey. Furthermore, many kinds of animals show differing food preferences at different times of the year.

68

Feeding habits do not serve only to prevent excessive competition within a species. The ever-present struggle for existence ensures that every conceivable source of nourishment is exploited. An infinite variety of structural adaptations with their corresponding behaviour patterns has therefore been evolved so that this is achieved.

The basic source of nourishment for the animal kingdom is provided by plant life which, in turn, utilises energy from sunlight for the synthesis of carbohydrates and proteins. Vegetable matter therefore forms the basis of the *food chains* of all animals. Some eat plants directly and they, in turn, are eaten by carnivorous forms. In general, a large number of plants supports smaller numbers of small herbivores which themselves are the food of even fewer but larger carnivores. Thus we have the concept of a pyramid of numbers having the least numerous but largest types at the apex. For example, microscopic plants or phytoplankton drifting in the surface waters of the oceans support smaller numbers of zooplankton. These provide for the appetites of small fishes themselves destined to be eaten by yet larger fish which form the food of seals. Occasionally, however, the food chain is short-circuited, as when whale-bone whalesfi lter off immense numbers of zooplankton in the form of the shrimp-like 'krill', *Euphausia superba*, which forms the staple diet of the world's largest animal.

In general, the larger carnivores have a slower reproductive rate than their herbivorous prey. Furthermore they tend to range further afield and are less strictly confined to one habitat than are herbivores. The ways in which animal numbers are regulated in nature are by no means clearly understood, although behaviour patterns certainly play a part.

Many aquatic animals have evolved mechanisms by which tiny planktonic organisms are filtered from the environment: the means by which this is achieved are almost as varied as those by which larger prey is caught. Many small planktonic animals are filter-feeders, using their powers of locomotion to take them to areas where food is plentiful. Many sessile forms, too, such as barnacles, annelid worms and bivalve molluscs have adopted filter-feeding methods. Filter-feeding may be achieved by the production of ciliary currents as in Protozoa and rotifers; by a net of tentacles as seen in *Hydra* and marine hydroids; by a ciliary field with mucus or a mucus net covering gill-slits. Most of the Crustacea employ a net of hairs or setae; this is either passed through the water by movements of the appendages to which the hairs are attached, or the hairs remain stationary and a current of water is driven through them.

Filter-feeding animals often possess sense organs for testing the chemical nature of the medium on which they are feeding and

The archer-fish 'shoots' its prey with a jet of water

cease to feed when these are unfavourably stimulated. But in the filtering apparatus itself, it is the physical characters of the food which determine whether it is accepted or rejected.

Baleen whales are not the only vertebrates that feed by filtering small organisms from the sea. Basking sharks do the same thing, and crabeater seals have serrated cusps on their teeth which enable them to filter mouthfuls of crustacea, whilst various birds, such as flamingoes, strain water and mud through their bills.

Filter-feeding does not occur among terrestrial animals of course, but the webs of spiders serve as a means of trapping insects in flight and innumerable fascinating modifications are found. Some of the most extreme occur in certain Australian and South African species which emerge at nightfall and whirl a thread weighted with a gummy globule until this strikes some passing insect, which is then hauled in.

Herbivorous animals have to be able to cope with much larger quantities of food than do insectivorous and carnivorous beasts. In

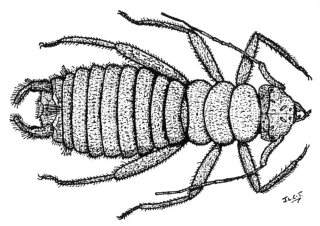

The parasitic earwig, *Arixenia esau* (male)
(length 2·5 cm.)

addition to dental cusps modified for grinding their food, ruminants possess special stomach caecae in which the food can be stored and bacterial action take place. Indeed not only is the anatomy, and especially the mouth parts of every animal adapted to a particular type of food, but much of its behaviour is modified for it. One has only to glance at the teeth of a cat, pig, horse or bat to know what kind of food is eaten, but the mode of locomotion and general behaviour of an animal is often an equally reliable guide. The same is true for almost any species, although occasionally the zoologist comes upon a puzzle.

For instance, I recently investigated some curious earwigs, *Arixenia esau*, apparently parasitic on bats in Malaya and the East

Indies, but was unable to determine the diet of the creatures. Experiments in the Niah Cave, Sarawak, have since proved that *Arixenia* feeds upon the epidermal products of the bat and will also attack and eat injured insects including members of its own species.

Sometimes smaller predators, such as wild dogs and wolves, by banding together, are able to kill herbivorous game animals even larger than themselves; but in general predatory species are bigger than their prey. Weasels and stoats provide an exception. There is, therefore, an optimum size for a carnivorous species. It must be strong and large enough to catch and kill its food; but if it is too big it will not be able to catch enough to support itself.

There is an optimum size too, for the herbivorous animals that form the prey, although this is not so closely defined by the environment. The Chinese proverb to the effect that large fowl cannot eat small grain is relevant here. An animal must also be big enough to migrate from one feeding ground to another. On the other hand a large number of small creatures can exploit a limited area much more thoroughly than a small number of larger forms.

Escape from Enemies

Einstweilen bis den Bau der Welt
Philosophie zusammenhält
Erhält sie das Getriebe
Durch Hunger und durch Liebe.
> J. C. F. SCHILLER (1759–1805)

This is somewhat misleading: the twin urges of 'hunger' and 'love' may be very potent, but they do not operate continuously. On the other hand, wild animals must be constantly alert to avoid enemies and not satisfy *their* hunger! This is so during play, when sunbathing, grooming themselves and even while sleeping. It is the natural state of affairs: in a similar way primitive peoples are constantly on guard against devils and demons. Freedom from the restrictions of taboo and the terrors of superstition and sorcery must surely constitute one of the greatest boons of civilisation.

Flight is the habitual response of the majority of animals to an enemy although some assume an absolute immobility that enables them to escape detection. In most vertebrates flight takes place only when the predator comes within a specific *'flight distance'*. This depends to some extent upon size and speed, but varies according

72

to circumstances. For example, whilst in South Africa, I have approached on horseback to within thirty yards of a blesbok. Had I been on foot, the antelope would never have let me get so close. Again, the flight distance of game animals to a vehicle is far less than to a man on his own. As an animal becomes tame the flight distance, within which it will not permit an enemy to approach, is gradually reduced. Antelopes can tell the difference between a hungry and a fully-fed lion and adjust their flight distance accordingly. If a predator approaches slowly, the prey will move off quietly, maintaining its flight distance. If the predator makes a dash, the prey bolts.

Of course this is a generalisation and each species has its own individual escape reaction. The rabbit dashes to its hole, the hare darts off following a zig-zag path, the pheasant flies into the air, the grebe dives into water, the young curlew sits quite still, trusting to its camouflage and the opossum shams death. Absolute stillness as well as quick escape reactions helps to avoid enemies.

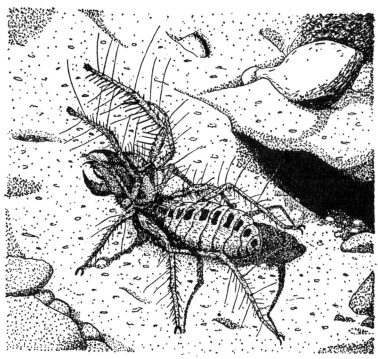

Defensive attitude of the false-spider, *Galeodes arabs*

73

Fighting

When an animal is approached to within a *'critical distance'* automatically it must stand and fight if it has not already fled. Hence the danger of following a wounded buffalo into thick bush: if the hunter gets within the critical distance, his quarry will certainly charge. Similarly a cornered rat or weasel will fight ferociously.

Most fighting, however, is intra-specific, concerned with mating and therefore seasonal. Harm to the species would follow if it invariably, or even frequently resulted in the death of one of the combatants. Indeed, threatening gestures and ceremonies are more common than actual fighting and are often sufficient to make a trespasser leave the territory of his rival. In the case of the stickleback, rival males adopt a vertical threat posture in which they appear to stand on their heads. This results from a ritualisation of sand-digging (a preliminary to the construction of the nest) which later became a *'displacement reaction'* (see p. 145) and is now employed as a sign-stimulus.

If two male sticklebacks are allowed to establish adjacent territories in a large aquarium, usually neither trespasses voluntarily on his neighbour's territory. But the situation can be provoked by capturing the fishes and placing them in separate test tubes. When the tubes are lowered together into the territory of the first stickleback, he will try to attack his rival through the double glass wall and the second will try equally franti-

Threatening attitude of a skunk before discharging its malodorous secretions

74

cally to escape. When both tubes are moved into the second territory, the situation is completely reversed.

Thus, in many animals the bark is worse than the bite. Two dogs may be excessively rude to one another when separated by a gate or fence. But if the gate is opened, a fight does not necessarily develop: the dogs may suddenly discover that they have other matters to attend to! On the other hand, the severity of the fights between male seals and stags in particular are notorious but even these do not usually result in the death of the defeated animal. In many kinds of animals, special weapons have been evolved solely for reproductive fighting. In the spring, male bitterlings develop horny warts on their heads with which they bump each other; the horns of the giraffe are reserved for social encounters, while predatory enemies are engaged with the hoofs. Rival rattlesnakes attempt to push each other over, but neither rattles nor poison fangs come into play during such disputes.

Male impalas fighting

The function of all this reproductive fighting is economy. Fighting, and the territorial behaviour with which it is associated, tends to ensure that the species is well distributed and prevents excessive competition for food. This is especially important in the case of 'nidicolous' birds such as sparrows and starlings which hatch in such a naked, defenceless state that their parents cannot leave them for long.

Occasionally inter-specific fighting between similar species results from misidentification, and erroneous attacks may occur where one species inadvertently presents one of the sign-stimuli normally releasing attack by another. Inter-specific fighting may also result from competition. For example, starlings and tree sparrows are known to drive other birds from their nesting holes. Sometimes there is even an hierarchy of species domination — for example, ibex dominate chamoix which, in turn, dominate the roe deer.

Peck-order

Within any social group there is usually a tyrant animal who dominates all others. He (or she, for tyrants are not confined to the male sex) is often spoken of as the 'alpha' animal. Below him are ranged his companions in order of rank, the lowest being called the 'omega'. In mixed groups, when the alpha animal is a female, she is usually superceded during the breeding season: but on the whole a tyrant who has been deposed finds great difficulty in becoming re-established.

In the chicken run, the alpha bird can peck all others without fear of retaliation and every bird is allowed to peck those below her in social rank. The poor omega cannot peck anyone with impunity. Nevertheless, her position is not without advantages, for she usually escapes attention from the alpha hen and the others at the top of the hierarchy. There must be a parallel here with human behaviour!

In colonies of rhesus monkeys each animal indicates its social rank by its posture and the way it carries its tail. The alpha monkey is accorded a *'social space'* into which none of its inferiors dares enter, with the exception of its chief concubine (usually the female who happens to be 'on heat' at that particular time). When a male animal, high in social rank, mates with a lowly female, she at once assumes the rank of her husband.

The hierarchial social system has an evolutionary advantage in that it reduces the amount of fighting that takes place, for individual animals naturally soon learn to avoid their superiors as much as possible! Respect for senior animals has educational value too, and young chimpanzees have been shown to learn more quickly from their social superiors than from teachers of low status.

The training of circus animals

Circuses provide a certain amount of interesting data for animal psychologists and the learning of tricks may benefit some captive animals because it keeps them alert.

Animals that feed little and often, like seals and sea-lions, can, of course, be bribed to perform their tricks. Dangerous carnivores such as lions and tigers, on the other hand, can be controlled only while their tamer exerts the authority of the alpha animal. The whip is an extension of the tamer's social space and he must judge the critical distance of his animals to a few centimetres, for within this distance their reaction changes from one of flight to defensive attack.

In contrast to the flight reaction, which may take place in any direction, defensive attack is directed only towards the tamer. Thus, by invoking its flight reaction, a lion can be manoeuvred so that it is behind a pedestal. The tamer then steps forwards and infringes the critical distance of his charge who moves forward to attack and, in so doing, climbs the pedestal. The trainer then steps back and the necessity for attack disappears so that the lion is left standing, bewildered, on the pedestal. After it has quietened down, it can be driven off the pedestal by again invoking its flight reaction. By repetition of this kind of manoeuvre the lion can gradually be taught to regard the pedestal as a resting place or refuge from the attentions of its superior, the tamer, and will return there whenever it has completed a trick. Later in training the pedestal can be replaced by a see-saw and the other paraphernalia of the circus ring.

The alpha animal is not necessarily the strongest; but it is usually the most imposing and imperturbable and thereby can intimidate its neighbours. The trainer himself does just this: he establishes himself as the alpha animal. Then the omega and others low in social rank may attempt to ingratiate themselves by performing tricks. But all the time the trainer has to watch out for the beta and gamma lions. He will never be able to teach them so much, yet if he turns his back for a second, one of them may take the opportunity to eliminate him and establish itself as tyrant!

A caged animal regards the cage as its territory. That is why anyone foolish enough to climb into a lion's or tiger's cage is inevitably attacked, for in this case territory and critical distance coincide.

The effect of learning

Learning naturally plays an important part both in fighting and in the establishment of a peck-order. Thus, when two hens meet for the first time, they usually fight: consequently one will win and the other lose. The next time they meet, they fight again, but this time the loser gives up sooner. As one fight follows another, one hen gradually acquires the habit of threatening and the other of running away. In this way each hen in a flock learns by degrees to accept a particular position in the hierarchy.

One of the conditions that causes abnormal behaviour among animals is the inability to adapt to a situation. We can say objectively that a person who is unable to adapt himself is frustrated. In addition to the obvious causes of fighting, as when one animal trespasses within another's territory or steals its food, aggressive behaviour may result from repression or frustration.*

An experiment was recently carried out on a herd of goats which had a well-established dominance order in competing for food. The goats were fed in pairs and the dominant animal always chased the subordinate one away so that it got very little food. Despite this frustration, the subordinate goat never showed any resistance. When the whole herd was frustrated by removal of their food for several hours before the test, the amount of aggression did increase but only in the dominant goats. This suggests that frustration leads to aggression only in situations where the individual has a habit of being aggressive.

Of course, hormones also play a part in aggressive behaviour but the situation is rather complicated. It might be supposed, for example, that in men an individual who had more male hormone might be more aggressive, and a person with smaller amounts more difficult to arouse, but there is no proof of this. In fact, there is some evidence to the contrary in that male and female nervous systems respond differently to the male hormone.

In an experiment to test the effect of hormones, two castrated male chimpanzees were kept in the same cage. In order to provoke aggressiveness a board was placed against the cage on each end of which was a cup containing a peanut. Both animals could therefore reach through and get a nut. Immediately afterwards a single cup with a peanut in it was placed on the board. Naturally the chimpanzees fought over it and soon developed an order of dominance. When the subordinate animal was given injections of male hormone, however, he revolted against the other and became dominant, retaining his position even after the hormone treatment was stopped. He was reduced to a subordinate rôle again by bringing a third animal into the cage. An injection of female hormone now had no

* Frustration may also quite frequently result in displacement activity (see p. 145).

78

effect on his behaviour, but he was once more raised to a position of dominance by the use of male hormone.

When this experiment was over, he was given female hormone again and this time he lost his dominant status. It was therefore concluded that the male hormone stimulates aggression and the female hormone reduces it.

In domesticating various birds and mammals, man has usually selected for decreased aggressiveness so that domestic breeds are easier to tame and handle. Certain breeds of dogs, however, such as terriers and bulldogs have for centuries been bred for fighting so it is clear that a tendency towards aggression is an hereditary characteristic. Even more important, however, is the effect of learning.

When two inexperienced mice are placed together they usually fight indifferently or not at all. Training can be achieved by placing one of them with an experienced fighter which attacks at once. As soon as he begins to fight back, the two are separated. Next day another mouse is held by the tail and bumped against the trainee who is stimulated to attack. At once the helpless stimulus mouse is removed so that the fight appears to have been successful. After several daily repetitions an untrained mouse is introduced to the new fighter who attacks at once and almost always wins. After this, no further training is necessary, although the trained fighter will attack more fiercely if briefly stimulated with a helpless mouse before each genuine fight.

Similar methods have been developed for the training of successful athletic or boxing champions. The novice first indulges in training bouts where no decision is reached. His coach or manager then arranges for him to begin his career with an easy victory, after which successively more formidable opponents are chosen. When he is ready for the big fight with someone trained like himself, both contestants will compete long and skilfully. Football coaches attempt to train their teams in the same way but since other coaches are doing the same, the procedure seldom works out in practice.

Surrender

Fierce and dangerous species usually have an instinctive gesture of surrender which they can use when necessary to inhibit the attack reaction of a stronger individual. A defeated wolf adopts an attitude of humility in which he exposes his vulnerable neck to a stronger rival. However 'enraged' that rival may be, he cannot bring himself to bite his humble opponent, although he may growl fiercely and bare his teeth.

We see the same thing in a dog fight. Whenever the weaker dog moves, the attack is resumed. After a time, however, the upper dog has to leave his 'trade mark' on the battlefield — for urinating is the ceremony which indicates his right of possession — and this gives the vanquished one a chance to escape.

Even when fighting, ravens, crows and other birds with formidable beaks are inhibited from pecking at each others eyes. Indeed the possessor of a tame raven need never fear that his pet will blind him, for the inhibition is strong even towards man. This inhibition is of value to a species possessing a formidable beak. In contrast, if two 'harmless' doves (which do not possess such inhibitions) are enclosed together so that the weaker cannot escape, murder will take place unless the birds are quickly separated. Normally a dove cannot inflict injury to any great degree. At the same time it has well-developed powers of flight so that a sign of surrender is not required. But if it is prevented from escaping it will be slowly, but inevitably pecked to death by its rival.

The same is true of 'harmless' herbivores such as roe deer, which probably cause more accidents in zoos than tigers do, because people do not recognise the slow approach of a buck as a dangerous attack.

Human beings hold up their hands in token of surrender. The Homeric warrior discarded his helmet and shield, falling on his knees as he offered his bare head in surrender to the enemy. Men, however, are less compelled by instinct than are other animals and until the days of chivalry it was not unusual for prisoners to be killed without mercy.

Even so, it is probably easier to kill millions at long range with bombs, explosive shells or botulinus toxin than it would be to bring oneself to slaughter a single defenceless prisoner with a knife. The more that remote control is employed in warfare, the less are cruel and bloodthirsty actions inhibited by instinct.

Chapter 7

Courtship and mating

REPRODUCTION in many marine animals such as anemones, worms, oysters and sea-urchins, consists merely of shedding the sexual products into the sea where fertilisation takes place. Although this type of behaviour is extremely simple, nevertheless the sexes must be in fairly close proximity to ensure union of egg and sperm, whose vitality is of limited duration. Almost all animals, however sedentary, have in their life-histories at least one brief, free-living stage during which dispersal takes place. Unlike plants, they are selective of their environments and their distribution is a matter of choice rather than of chance. Consequently, since members of the same species naturally tend to select the same habitat, external fertilisation is not quite so haphazard as at first appears.

Synchronisation

Furthermore, the reproductive activity of the sexes must be synchronised and, in marine forms, is frequently correlated with the tides and the phases of the moon. One of the most dramatic examples is afforded by the Palolo worm, *Leodice viridis*, which lives among coral reefs in the Pacific Ocean. In the breeding season the hind part of the worm is packed with reproductive cells. At the last quarter of the moon in October and November, it breaks away and floats upwards to the surface of the sea where the genital products are discharged and fertilisation takes place. Spawning takes place at low tide on several successive days, and so regular is the appearance of the worms that the natives, who esteem them a great delicacy, know just when to prepare their boats and nets.

The lunar breeding of the luminous worm, *Odontosyllis enopla*, in the West Indies has an unexpected historical interest. This worm swarms at the surface of the Atlantic during the night at the third quarter of the moon and the shining light from the females attracts the males. The luminescent glow at the surface of the sea lasts only

81

five or ten minutes: females appear first at the water surface and emit a stream of brilliantly luminous secretion with the eggs. Males then rush in with short, intermittent flashes.

Now, on 11th October, 1492, at 22.00 hours a mysterious light was seen from the poop of Christopher Columbus's ship, the

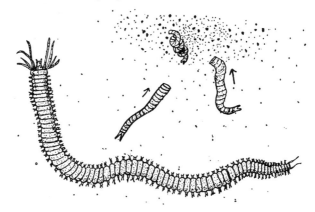

The Palolo worm, *Leodice viridis*

Santa Maria, just in the region where this occurs. It was compared with the flame of a small candle alternately raised and lowered. On that night the moon was one day from her third quarter. It has been suggested that this may be a point of evidence of first importance towards settling the problem of the landfall of Columbus in the West Indies.

Similar examples of regular spawning by other species of worm have been cited from other regions and the mollusc, *Chiton*, breeds only at the time of full moon in certain parts of the world.

The larvae of the oyster swarm about eight days after the eggs have been fertilised. They lead a short floating life, a dispersal phase (see Chapter 8) and then settle down. In Holland, for example, swarming mostly occurs each year between June 26th and July 10th, about ten days after the full or new moon. This is because spawning takes place at spring tide; but how the tides affect the oyster is not known. It may be that the intensity of light passing through the water reaches a maximum, or perhaps the animals are affected by the unusually large oscillations in the pressure of the water at this time.

The grunion, *Leuresthes tenuis*, spawns during high spring tides. The little fishes come ashore on the top of a wave, lie for a moment

PLATE IX

Hairy Imperial spider of Australia catching
its prey by whirling a line and sticky globule

PLATE X

After mating the
female mantis devours
the helpless male

PLATE XI

Wood ants dragging a dead worm to their nest

PLATE XII

Nurse bees feeding the grubs in the cells of the brood comb

on the sand and drop back into the sea with the successive wave. The eggs develop in the dry sand, hatching when they are again covered with water at the next spring tide.

In birds and mammals the timing of reproduction is more complicated. In the majority of cases the main environmental factor is the gradually increasing amount of daylight in late winter. This stimulates the pituitary gland in the brain to secrete a hormone which is discharged into the blood stream and thereby affects the sex-glands. These, in turn, secrete sex-hormones which influence the central nervous system and bring about the first stages of reproductive behaviour. Timing may not be very accurate: for example, in pigeons the male is usually further advanced than the female, but his persistent courtship speeds up her development. This occurs even when two birds are separated in adjoining cages. Under such conditions the female can still be induced to lay eggs.

In higher animals, fertilisation involves both synchronisation and mating — that is, bodily contact between the sexes. Normally however, animals tend to avoid contact with one another, a behavioural adaptation that no doubt forms part of their defence against predators and, at the same time, probably tends to reduce the transmission of parasites and disease. One of the functions of courtship, therefore, is to break down these natural inhibitions.

In addition, courtship results in animals coming together and orientating themselves so that their genital organs are in contact. Finally it has the important task of ensuring reproductive isolation and preventing cross-breeding.

Hybridisation is best avoided because different species have widely differing gene complexes and their delicately balanced growth patterns are easily disturbed. Secondly, fertilised eggs may be produced which do not develop properly or perhaps die when they should begin to grow. Hybrids are usually less successful and compete at a disadvantage with the parent species as these are naturally well adapted to their own particular ecological niches. Finally even if they do manage to survive and develop, hybrids are frequently infertile. Let us now consider how these various functions are achieved.

Finding a mate

For bisexual animals, a necessity for survival of the species is the discovery of a suitable mate. Recognition of a receptive partner is the first link in the chain of events leading to union of the sex-cells. Far from being a random search, mate-finding in higher animals is a highly organised process which involves one or more of the senses of sight, smell, sound, touch and even taste.

Vision is the primary factor for innumerable diurnal species, and some nocturnal animals such as owls and certain insects, have special lenses which enable them to find a mate by starlight. Fireflies and many of the inhabitants of the ocean depths find their mates by luminescence. Sea-cows and whales rely upon chemical trails for mate-finding and on land the importance of scent in bringing the sexes together can hardly be exaggerated. Male moths have been known to fly upwind for several miles to a female.

In birds, where the phenomena of display and courtship attain a complexity unrivalled except by man, song is often an initial feature of the ritual which first attracts and excites the female, as it does in the case of frogs and toads, cicadas, crickets and grasshoppers. In fact, many of the sign stimuli by which male animals indicate their territories and repel other males, serve also to advertise their presence to females.

Persuasion

Having recognised a potential mate, the next hurdle for the male is to bring her into close proximity. The female is generally more valuable to the species than is the male, for in most cases she carries the eggs after mating has taken place and also plays a larger part in protecting the young. In addition the male is usually capable of fertilising more than one female. It is not at all surprising, therefore, that the female requires some persuading and the male has the more active rôle in courtship.

Indeed, he is by no means always successful at first and may have to repeat his releaser signals over and over again before he can induce the female to mate with him. There is often a genuine reluctance on the part of the female sex which is probably in the interests of biological economy, for unless conditions are really suitable for the rearing of young she is seldom receptive.

Male kestrel passing prey to female

Apart from this, feminine coyness probably stimulates the male. In animal as well as in human courtship, a show of resistance or a chase often serves to encourage the male and lead him on.

Displacement-preening, courtship and group display among avocets

When a female spotted turtle is approached by a male, her usual response is to move away; but she looks coyly over her shoulder all the while, as though to make sure that he is following her. In the same way the hen redshank will often suffer the approach of the cock and then shy away like a startled horse. She generally runs in circles, however, as though the pursuit were not wholly disagreeable. In the case of the red deer, the hind frequently runs away when

The lapwing displays to his mate

approached by the stag, but she soon stops and waits for him, licks him, and then runs on again, only to wait once more for his approach.

The male sex is frequently aggressive in defence of territory and consequently courtship in females often takes the form of reactions which tend to avoid provoking, or prevent attack. For example, female gulls show 'infantile' behaviour reminiscent of the

85

appeasement employed by the young (p. 137). Ceremonial begging for food by females and the presentation of food by the male gulls are behaviour patterns carried over from infancy. In avocets, both species preen their feathers in a hasty, 'nervous' fashion during courtship, after which the female adopts a characteristic flattened attitude which is the sign that she is ready to mate.

In scorpions and spiders, it is the male who has to appease his spouse so that she does not eat him. Courtship in scorpions takes the form of a dance or 'promenade à deux'. On finding a female, the male grasps her claws with his and walks sideways or backwards while she follows, usually without reluctance. When the dancing pair reach a suitably firm surface, which the male apparently detects with his pectines (p. 17), he deposits a capsule of sperms, known as a *'spermatophore'*, on the ground and forcibly jerks his partner over it. She lowers her body and the spermatophore

Courtship display in Adelie penguins

becomes inserted in her genital aperture. Mating is similar in the curious little false-scorpions or Chelonethi, to be found beneath the bark of trees, and in leaf litter all over the world.

Spiders are nearly always on the offensive and are ready to kill and eat most animals of suitable size that come within range. They are inveterate cannibals, so it is obvious that mating must be a hazardous undertaking fraught with real danger, particularly to the male who is usually smaller and weaker than his intended mate. Indeed, he will almost certainly be devoured unless he succeeds in allaying temporarily the carnivorous instincts of the female, and this he must do before he ventures within reach of her rapacious jaws. It is of utmost importance to the male to establish his identity so that he is not treated like an insect victim, and thereafter courtship must proceed until the female has been stimulated to a state in which her sexual instincts have been aroused so that she will permit

86

mating to take place. Consequently, whichever of the senses is the one on which the species chiefly relies for the capture of its prey is the sense most employed in courtship. Male jumping-spiders and wolf-spiders make use of visual signs, short-sighted and nocturnal species of contact stimuli, web spinners use distinctive tweaks and vibrations of the threads of the snare, and so on.

The mating procedure of spiders is quite unique, for when the male reaches maturity he weaves a small pad of silk on which a drop

Courtship dance of scorpions

of sperm is deposited and this is sucked up by the specially modified *'pedipalps'* or hands which in due course are inserted into the vagina of the female. Each species has a palp with its own distinctive shape, a diagnostic character essential for accurate identification.

In most wolf-spiders the pedipalps and front legs are provided with an ornamentation of hair that contrasts sharply with the rest of the body. The male stands before the female waving these simultaneously or alternately in a kind of semaphore courtship. One species found on Staten Island, Argentina, makes a curious purring noise at mating time by drumming on dead leaves with its palps. It is probable that in this case the female appreciates the vibrations at

87

some distance. Even more dramatic are the courting dances of male jumping-spiders. In the tropical species, *Hasarius adansoni*, found in many hothouses in Britain, the male is a handsome, squat, glossy black and brown spider with conspicuous white markings on the pedipalps, abdomen and distal limb segments. During courtship he advances slowly in zig-zag fashion, waving his palps up and down. When the female, who is a sombre brown colour, turns towards him he stops and remains motionless with his large forelegs held horizontally above the ground. Then he moves forward again. As he nears the female he may jump rapidly sideways or backwards. Again and again this display continues until at last he is permitted to insert first one and then the other of his pedipalps.

Courtship dance of the jumping-spider, *Hasarius adansoni*

Among web-builders, courtship usually consists of the male telegraphing to the female occupant of a web by tweaking the threads as he approaches, but in later stages a tactile stroking of her body precedes mating. This routine may constitute a tactile display almost equal in interest to the visual displays of the long-sighted hunting spiders.

In ethological terminology, the function of courtship is to provide releaser stimuli for the mating instinct which at the same time block hunger drives. The concept of recognition may not in fact be necessary.

Polygamy is the custom among spiders and it is indeed wise for the male to retreat hastily immediately copulation is accomplished.

Occasionally the sexes appear to live together peacefully, but experiment has shown that in the case of the garden spider, *Meta reticulata*, this apparent faithfulness is fictitious and males may visit the web of more than one female. In this species the males often kill one another. Since courtship is deferred until the female is engaged in trussing a victim or eating a meal, it is not uncommon to see it taking place over the dead body of a vanquished rival.

In robber-flies (Asilidae) the male presents his formidable mate with food, and fertilises her while her attention is momentarily engaged in eating. Similar behaviour has been recorded in mantids and spiders. In birds, begging and the acceptance of food by the female are juvenile traits which inhibit aggression by the male.

One is constantly impressed by the economy exercised in the number of behaviour patterns used by animals. Releasers and behaviour patterns originally devised for one particular situation are later employed in quite different circumstances. For example, many of the actions of earlier courtship in birds are found afterwards among nest-relief ceremonies.

Reproductive isolation

The signals used for attraction, persuasion, appeasement and synchronisation vary in different species. Consequently crossbreeding does not occur even where territories overlap.

There may be temporary lack of recognition as when a male stickleback begins to court a young tench whose deep body he mistakes for the swollen abdomen of a female of his own species. In a similar way a male grayling butterfly may begin to court another

Smooth Newts (from above)

Great Warty Newts
Courtship among newts

kind of butterfly or even a falling leaf. Such mistakes do not long persist, however, because the recipient of these attentions invariably reacts in the wrong way; for each species has its own sign language, and the brief romance is brought to a sudden halt.

Related species often show similar patterns of courtship behaviour which differ chiefly in the *tempo* at which they are carried out. For example, the male of one species of fruit-fly may vibrate its wings rapidly, thereby wafting a scent stimulus to the female; while the same movements, repeated more slowly by the males of a related species, provide a purely visual stimulus. Similarly, the displays of various species of fiddler-crab may differ primarily in the speed at which they are performed.

Differences in courtship and mating behaviour may be due either to the evolution of different languages which prevent hybridisation, or else they may have arisen as a result of geographical separation. In either case, distinctiveness has functional advantages.

Bower-birds and their displays

The brilliantly coloured bower-birds of Australia, New Guinea and the neighbouring islands build display-grounds and decorate them with various objects such as flowers, stones and shells. The bower of each species is built on the ground and has no connection with the nest which is made in a tree, often some distance away and usually later in the season. Nevertheless, it is believed that the display habits of bower-birds, however bizarre they may appear, are no more than an extraordinary elaboration of the territorial behaviour found in other kinds of birds. All degrees of intergradation occur between the simplest forms of display and the elaborate colour-selection, rhythmical noisy dances and architectural creations of the bower-birds.

One species, the satin bower-bird, *Ptilonorhynchus violaceus* of eastern Australia constructs a bower with two parallel walls of arched twigs. On one side of it is a display-ground in which is strewn a startling variety of coloured decorations which are evidently chosen with great discrimination for they are always blue, green, yellow, brown or grey in colour. A well-decorated display-ground at the height of the season presents a brilliant splash of colour on the otherwise sombre forest floor. It may contain up to seventy blue parrots' feathers, flowers, fragments of glass, crockery, rags, paper, shells, wasp-nests and so on.

Display begins at sunrise and may occur throughout the day, being interrupted by intervals during which the birds feed, bathe, preen, or call from branches above the territory. The male stands squarely on his territory, making a whirring noise that resembles the sound of a mechanical toy, arches his tail fanwise and stiffens

The satin bower-bird, *Ptilonorhynchus violaceus*, on its display ground

his wings at the same time holding his head low with neck erect. His plumage is said to glisten magnificently in the sunshine, whilst his blue eyes bulge and are suffused with rose-red.

The sombre female starts convulsively from time to time and may utter a few guttural notes. Occasionally she will rearrange the disordered twigs of the bower while the display is in progress. Meantime the male shies violently sideways, hops or runs quickly forwards and backwards. Then he suddenly snatches up one of the display objects and hops stiffly around, the decoration in his beak not in any way detracting from his vocal efficiency.

Satin-bower birds also have the habit of painting or plastering the inner walls of their bower with pulped fruit and other plant material chewed into a paste. Birds have even been known to steal charcoal and washing-blue for this purpose! Sometimes a piece of bark is held in the beak and used as a tool to wedge the 'paint' into position, a unique feature in their behaviour.

The spotted bower-bird, *Chlamydera maculata*, also makes use of human property, for silver coins, jewellery and car keys are not infrequently to be seen in its bowers. The Queensland gardener bower-bird, *Prionodura newtonia*, however, builds a bower which may reach a height of about nine feet which it decorates entirely with living orchids.

Many people who have studied bower-birds have failed to appreciate the utilitarian significance of their displays and have consequently assumed that the birds must possess a unique sense of artistry and aestheticism. This is, of course, quite unjustified: the fact that some species may select objects that appeal to man's sense of beauty is no proof that such articles have a similar subjective influence on the bird. Although by no means lacking in beauty, bower-birds do not possess the magnificent plumes of birds-of-paradise. Much of the display has been transferred from the bird to its territory but the instinctive nature of the behaviour is not altered.

The nature of instinct

Behaviour does not imply any conscious foresight or deliberate interest on the part of the animals that exhibit it. Except for man and possibly, to some extent, apes and a few other mammals, behaviour consists almost exclusively of reactions to external and internal stimuli. Physiological need engenders the *'drive'* or initial motivation which, in turn, seeks an outlet by 'appetitive behaviour'. This may take the form of locomotory responses — 'seeking' food, a mate and so on — or display. If all goes well the goal or *'consummatory act'* will be

Posture of rutting male rabbit displaying his white underside and sending towards his desired partner a jet of urine that seldom misses

released by the appropriate sign stimuli and the pent-up *'specific action potential'* dissipated.

Performance of the consummatory act does not necessarily imply that the ultimate function of the behaviour pattern has been achieved. For example, one can feel satisfied by a good meal long before digestion and assimilation have rendered the food available to the tissues of the body. Conversely I well remember, when taking part in an expedition to N.W. Iceland some years ago, how little satisfaction we obtained from our concentrated rations. Until we had swallowed a pint of hot tea each, we did not feel that we had really had a meal at all.

Courtship among African elephants

Effects are never brought into play as the causes of behaviour patterns. A complex instinct such as reproduction consists of an hierarchy of simpler units released at different levels of excitation and forming a series or chain of reflex actions, each stimulated by the one immediately preceding it. In the courtship of the stickle-back, the appearance of a female bearing the sign-stimulus of a swollen abdomen, releases a 'zig-zag' dance from the male. This signal releases courting by the female who swims beside him. He now leads the way to the nest, she follows, he indicates the entrance by pointing with his head and she enters. This is the stimulus for the male to tremble and prod the female with his snout which in

93

turn, releases spawning after which the eggs are fertilised and the female is chased away. The male now returns, repairs the nest and adjusts the eggs.

In a similar way, the prey of the orb-web spider is dealt with by a series of chain reflexes. The struggles of a victim in the web are the stimulus for a long bite and the taste experienced stimulates the enshrouding of the prey. The silk bands provide a tactile stimulus for the reflex of the short bite, which in turn produces a stimulus for the carrying reflex: small insects are carried to the hub of the web in the chelicerae, while heavier prey is carried on a thread from the spinnerets and supported by a hind leg. When a lifeless inedible object touches the web it is usually cut out and allowed to fall to the ground, as are formidable and dangerous insects such as wasps and bees, whereas suitable prey is bitten and then wrapped up, to be eaten later.

Each facet of the behaviour sequence must be carried out at the appointed time before the next can be released. The reproductive behaviour of the stickleback, however, did not begin with courtship and mating. Some weeks before, the male fish had assumed his scarlet nuptial livery, established a territory and driven off rival males. He had also dug a hole and constructed a nest of water-weed which he guarded until a gravid female, herself influenced by an inner drive emanating from her physiological condition, showed the appetitive behaviour as a result of which she swam into his territory.

The complexity of animal behaviour becomes understandable only when analysis such as this breaks it down into a series of reflex actions, each of which can be tested experimentally by the use of models.

Chapter 8

Migration

It seemed to bear a charmed life in its languid blood
and imperceptible motions; yet it was not so inactive as
it seemed; it held a regular and monotonous course:
inch by inch it traversed the little orbit of its domains,
taking months to accomplish the whole gyration. It was
a restless voyager that tortoise!

E. BULWER-LYTTON (1834)

THE DISTRIBUTION in the world of any group of animals depends both upon its place of origin and its power of spread-
ing. Every species must be able to disperse to a certain
extent, to avoid overcrowding and overcome other vicissitudes such
as attacks by enemies, climatic changes, drought, flooding and so on
which, sooner or later, make every place at least temporarily
uninhabitable.

Dispersal normally takes place by locomotion and many animals
have active as well as passive stages in their life history. Sessile
animals such as corals, barnacles, sea-lilies and scale-insects have a
free-living larval phase of development, while others such as crabs,
star-fishes and lug-worms, which tend to be somewhat restricted as
adults, are also distributed as larvae. Animals which are restricted
in their young stages such as the Palolo worm mentioned above
(p. 81), and the majority of insects become dispersed as adults
since their larvae are flightless.

So do frogs, which will return to the same pond year after year
in the breeding season. Though the owners may plant laburnum,
hawthorn and flowering shrubs; though their children learn to
skate there, and old sportsmen enjoy curling matches in the winter,
these are mere diversions. Every spring the frogs assert their rights
and arrive in their hundreds. And every summer thousands of tad-
poles delight the youth of the neighbourhood and innumerable tiny
frogs, clean and shining, leave the water to invade the surrounding

95

countryside. Many leave, but few, alas, return; the life of a small frog qualifies for no insurance! It is not known for certain how frogs find their way to a pond. Some say that it is the smell of the water which attracts them, but this has not yet been proved.

Many animals become dispersed accidentally whilst they are searching for food: others may be transported for long distances by wind and there are numerous cases of incidental dispersal of the inhabitants of logs floating in the sea, not to mention those carried to new regions by human agency. In this chapter, however, we are concerned only with distribution caused by the positive behaviour of animals themselves.

Emigration

When the pressure exerted by a species on its environment increases as a result of overcrowding, *'irruptions'* or *'emigrations'* may occur. Examples are afforded by centipedes and millipedes (see p. 34), locusts, termites, dragonflies, ants, butterflies and other insects, populations of which increase to vast numbers and then invade new areas. In the case of most kinds of locust, breeding may continue in the newly exploited regions for several generations, but for climatic reasons which are not yet fully understood, the emigrants eventually die out and only a small resident population of the species remains in the original outbreak area.

In Arctic regions, cyclical variations in numbers leading to mass emigrations are shown by creatures such as lemmings, voles and snow-shoe rabbits. These are followed by fluctuations in the numbers of their predators which include the lynx and snowy owl. Two or three main cycles seem to occur. First, there is a four-year cycle in the numbers of various mammals and birds in the tundra based on the lemming; secondly there is a four-year cycle in the animals of the open forest and grassland, found particularly in the belt between the tundra and the main coniferous forests. This is based on the vole. Thirdly, there is a ten-year cycle in the snow-shoe rabbit and other animals of the northern forest regions of North America.

It has been suggested that the dominant rodent interacts with its specialised vegetable food supply and the regularity of the cycles may be due to the fact that basic predator-prey oscillations, synchronised by the interaction of lunar and solar cycles, are less disturbed by incidental factors than in other parts of the world. In contrast, the equatorial rain-forest, because of its extreme complexity, has the greatest inherent stability of any bio-geographical region. A tremendous richness of species tends to give a buffering effect to any unusual population change.

Cyclical fluctuations in numbers are a means by which animal populations are adjusted to periodic changes in environmental conditions. Until the population has reached its maximum density the full effects of predation, starvation and epidemic disease do not come into play. Starvation and epidemics, at least, will weaken all the members of the population and it may be better for the species that a part of the crowded population should migrate and allow those that are left to form a healthy, but less numerous breeding stock. Thus, although natural selection may eliminate the individuals that migrate, it will tend to favour populations showing the migratory instinct.

True emigrants seldom return. The lemmings of Norway move always to the west until they reach the sea into which they plunge and are drowned in myriads. Their movement may be occasioned by food shortage and overcrowding, accompanied by a forced expulsion of part of the colony, and it is associated with a sort of mass hysteria, for the emigrants appear to show no 'fear' of enemies, the sea, or of death itself. They cannot stop their massed advance for they are forced always onwards by the owners of the territories they happen to pass. Parallel examples are afforded by the migratory spring-buck of S. Africa and other deer, moose, rats, birds, such as waxwing and Pallas' sand grouse, and various other animals. Emigrants almost always die; only slow drift migrations such as that of the brown rat into Europe (p. 65) are attended with success and this may be due to the fact either that they usually accompany slow climatic changes, or else the species has been introduced into a favourable area in which there is little competition from other species. Although millions of brown rats were drowned in swimming the Volga, the survivors continued their westward march and multiplied so rapidly that before long they had colonised the whole continent of Europe. They moved swiftly through the Ukraine, southern Poland and Bohemia. In 1740 another army of rats was reported as having arrived in East Prussia: in 1773 they reached Paris. During the nineteenth century the brown rat arrived in force in North America, crossed the continent and reached the Pacific coast by 1851. In this case, the black rat, itself an earlier introduction, gave way in face of the competition from its more successful rival.

97

The influence of population density on the migratory instinct is illustrated by invertebrate animals too. When numbers of the 'water-flea', *Daphnia pulex*, are high and food supply is short, fewer eggs are laid so that the next generation is less numerous. Conversely, when numbers are low, the reproductive rate increases. Again, in rice-weevils, *Calandra oryzae*, emigration occurs when numbers rise beyond a certain level. If it is prevented, however, the females lay fewer eggs and the adults eat many rice grains already inhabited by larvae. Hence, when crowded, each adult gives rise to fewer surviving offspring.

The water-flea, *Daphnia pulex* (length about 1 mm)

Just as emigration and territorial behaviour can prevent over-crowding and reduce numbers, so can physiological control of the birth-rate ensure that population densities are kept near the optimum for any particular habitat.

Nomadism

A life of wandering is rare amongst lower animals, most of which have a marked 'homing instinct'. To the casual holiday-maker, limpets appear almost as fixtures scarcely less permanent or painful to bare feet than the jagged rocks on which they live. When covered by the sea, however, these animals frequently move about and browse upon algae, returning to their 'homes' when the tide falls. This is necessary because the margins of their shells grow and are worn to conform with the irregularities of the rock; and if water were not retained around their gills while the tide was out, they would die from desiccation. The exact nature of the homing instinct by which limpets return to the same place time after time, has so far defied analysis. It probably results from a muscular memory of the direction and distance travelled.

Marine fishes tend to be migratory rather than nomadic in habit and have special feeding grounds and spawning areas although they may wander from one of these to another. Many reptiles and amphibians are truly nomadic and constantly change their feeding and breeding areas, but among the birds nomadism is rare. Even the frigate bird 'before whose flight all distance vanishes' so that it may 'breakfast at the Senegal and dine in America' is never beyond reach of its home and has no occasion to shift its quarters in order to exploit a particular hunting ground.

Amongst mammals, however, nomadism is more common, especially in arid areas and deserts. Where the vegetation is insufficient to support a permanent population, the inhabitants have to travel far from one feeding ground to another. Again, many ungulates, such as the moose, have comparatively restricted winter quarters yet are nomadic over a wide area for the remainder of the year.

Diurnal migration in plankton

Many aquatic organisms show a periodic ascent and descent in the water in which they live. Several species of Crustacea, for example, migrate upwards at night, some at dusk or dawn, and a few during the day. Diurnal migration in plankton (the community of organisms inhabiting the surface waters of lakes and oceans) is a complex phenomenon. The behaviour of related species may vary considerably, and during its life-history even the same animal may show differing responses to identical stimuli.

Increase in temperature results in a tendency for the little 'water-flea', *Daphnia pulex*, to swim downwards away from the light. The reverse occurs with decreasing temperature, and below 12° C. *Daphnia* swims towards light of all intensities. Both increase in light and temperature result in the animals swimming downwards during the day. At night, however, decreased illumination and lower temperatures lead to the reverse response, and they move upwards. It is believed that reversal of the response to gravity with change in light-intensity is a predominant factor affecting diurnal migration in this species. In addition, however, *Daphnia* shows a diurnal periodicity in specific gravity. This is lowest in the early morning, and in consequence *Daphnia* tends to float upwards from deeper water to the surface where it finds a plentiful supply of the algae on which it feeds. After a meal, during which its density increases, it sinks slowly again. The diurnal rhythm therefore also depends in part upon variation in food supply, which itself is dependent upon light as well as temperature. The periodic rise and fall towards and away from the surface waters is complicated in addition by the fact that after the brood pouch has emptied, there is a temporary decrease in specific gravity.

Another fresh-water crustacean, *Cyclops albidus*, normally swims downwards after exposure to light. The response becomes negative in darkness, however, so that the animals swim upwards at night, but after a time there is a spontaneous reversal again even if there is no change in external conditions. Similar changes occur in the aquatic larvae of the gnats, *Corethra* spp. *Arcella*, a little fresh-water protozoan, (p. 7) shows a rhythm of sinking and floating, depending on its oxygen requirements; and innumerable other examples could be quoted.

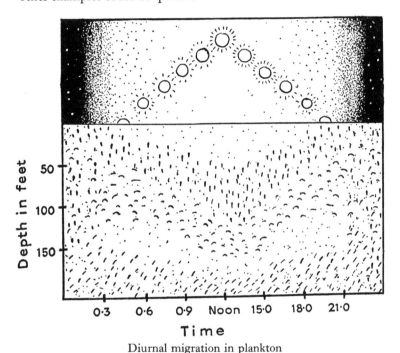

Diurnal migration in plankton

Plankton migration is infinitely more important in the case of marine animals. Specimens of the crustacean *Acartia* sp. taken from surface water initially exhibit varying responses to light, gravity, and temperature that differ from those of specimens from deeper water, although later all react in the same way. Here there is a physiological rhythm of negative and positive responses to gravity which is not directly related to external changes in the environment.

If diurnal migration is correlated with light intensity as has been suggested, it is reasonable to expect that there should be a relationship between the transparency of the water and the depth to which the plankton migrates, and it has indeed been shown that planktonic animals are to be found deeper in the sea on sunny days, or when the water is particularly clear. Again some species congregate on the surface, especially on moonless nights, and consequently fishermen shoot their drift-nets at night because then the herrings come to the surface to feed.

It must be emphasised, however, that each species has its own way of performing vertical movements, and no general explanation is possible. Changes in response to gravity with light and temperature are probably not sufficiently widespread to be considered of universal significance.

A parallel is afforded by the behaviour of starlings and other birds which roost in trees and buildings during the night, but fly to their feeding areas in the open country at daybreak.

Seasonal migrations

Regular migrations from one place to another *and back* (in this respect they differ from emigrations from which there is no return) occur in birds, whales, seals, bats, fishes, cuttlefish, some butterflies and moths, dragonflies and hoverflies.

Edible crabs migrate from the shore to deep water in the autumn and return in February after spawning. The females carry their eggs with them attached to their abdomens and in this state are known as 'berried crabs'. After the eggs have hatched, the adults moult and return to deep water. They do not, however, always return to the same part of the shore. The same is true of many fishes which migrate to coastal waters in the breeding season.

Land crabs, robber-crabs and terrestrial hermit-crabs, on the other hand, migrate to the sea to breed and then return to the shore, the young following as soon as they are old enough. The movements of the majority of insects are emigratory, but in the United States the monarch butterfly, which is a very long-lived species, migrates north for egg-laying and then flies south again in the autumn. Similarly in Europe the red admiral migrates north to breed and returns to winter quarters in the south.

Migrating Lepidoptera nearly always move within twenty feet of the ground and it appears unlikely that wind direction determines their movement to any great extent. If an insect flies at a fixed angle to the sun, its direction will change slowly during the day unless it is able to allow for the change in angle necessitated by the apparent solar movement.

Although at present neither the external cause nor the internal mechanism of insect migration is known, time-compensated solar navigation has been established in bees, wolf-spiders, and sand-hoppers as well as in birds (p. 106). It does not seem improbable, therefore, that it may also account for the orientation of migrating insects.

During the last decade, research on locusts has shown that long distance movements of swarms take place high in the air where wind speeds are often greater than the maximum speed of flight. Consequently locusts tend to move into areas of low barometric pressure where rain is most likely to fall. The complicated reactions by which the insects maintain a constant angle with respect to the sun, which previously attracted so much attention from entomologists, presumably serve merely to keep the swarm together, and exert little effect upon its ultimate displacement. So, after nearly 3,000 years, the observations recorded in the Book of Exodus are confirmed. An east wind brought the plague of locusts to Egypt and a west wind drove them into the Red Sea.

Fishes often undertake seasonal migrations. For example, cod spawn in the north-west Atlantic where the cold, relatively fresh water of the northern currents meets the warmer and more saline Gulf Stream from the south. Salmon, chad, sturgeon, etc. spawn in fresh water and frequently die there: the king salmon may travel 2,000 miles from the sea to spawning beds in Yukon. On the other hand the European eel breeds in the Sargasso Sea whence the young migrate to Europe, a distance of some 2–3,000 miles, taking about three years to complete the journey. American eels breed in the same area.

The free eggs of eels have not yet been found, but it is known that they hatch into larval forms so unlike their parents that they were originally believed to be a different species and were given the name of '*Leptocephalus*', meaning 'thin head'. These vary from one quarter to three inches in length, according to age, are bilaterally flattened resembling a leaf in shape and, despite the presence of 100 or more segments, are quite transparent. In fact, their invisibility probably enables them to elude many a hungry predator during the hazardous journey.

On reaching the Continental shelf, metamorphosis takes place and a typical cylindrical form is acquired. The transition was first discovered by observation of many specimens brought to the sur-

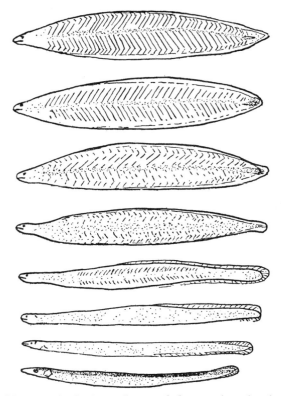

Metamorphosis from *Leptocephalus* to elver in the
common eel

face by whirlpools in the Straits of Messina. 'Elvers' as the young
eels are now called, ascend our rivers in countless numbers. They
are obliged to adjust their bodies so that the water passes equally on
both sides and this keeps them on a straight course upstream. As
they wriggle along the bottom provides them with a point of
reference relative to the flow of the stream (see p. 11). Elvers have
even been reported in enormous numbers at the foot of the
Niagara Falls, striving vainly to surmount this impossible obstacle.

Eels remain in fresh water, feeding and growing for several
years. The difference between the sexes becomes apparent only
when they are about six years old and the females begin to grow
more strongly than the males. Males assume breeding dress on
reaching a length of 12–20 inches that is, after 5½–6½ years in fresh
water, females after 6½–8½ years, by which time they have grown to

an even larger size. Eels over three feet in length have probably lived for ten or twelve years since the elver stage. Sooner or later, however, the reproductive instinct overtakes them; they become silver in colour, their eyes enlarge and they set out on a return journey to the Sargasso Sea. Those that reach their destination presumably spawn and die, for none return. It has recently been suggested that the common eels of Europe may be the progeny of American parents and may not therefore reproduce themselves. The eels of North America, however, must return to the breeding area.

Amphibians — frogs, toads and newts — migrate to fresh water for breeding and seasonal migrations also occur in reptiles. The female sea-snakes of the Indian Ocean migrate to land for the birth and rearing of their young. They make nurseries in rocky hollows on low islands within their hunting territories. Green turtles migrate in large droves during the breeding season. Some travel distances of 800 miles or more to Ascension Island. Like birds, individual turtles are believed to frequent the same breeding place year after year.

There are numerous instances of migration for breeding purposes among mammals. Caribou may travel 500 miles from winter retreats to their pairing grounds, and mule-deer may cover as much as 150 miles. The migratory spring-buck of South Africa are habitually nomadic as we have seen, but they migrate to a special part of their territory to give birth to the young. Similar movements occur in kudu, hippopotamus, elephants, bats, whales, seals and sea-lions to mention only a few. The formation of seal 'rookeries' is directly related to the limited space available for nurseries, and territorial behaviour is extremely important in these animals.

Bird migration

So when inclement winters vex the plain,
With piercing frosts, or thick descending rain,
To warmer seas the Cranes embodied fly,
With noise and order through the midway sky.
HOMER (12th century B.C.)
The Iliad, Bk. III, Trans. A. Pope, London, 1717

Allusions to the migratory movements of birds are found in the literature of all ages and nations. In the Book of Job (XXXIX, v. 26) we find the well-known passage: 'Doth the stork fly by Thy wisdom, and stretch her wings towards the south,' and in Jeremiah

(VIII, v. 7) the prophet declares 'The stork in heaven knoweth her appointed times; and the turtle-dove, and the crane, and the swallow, observe the time of their coming.' Anacreon (5th century B.C.) welcomed the return of the swallows in spring, and was correct in his assumption that Egypt was one of their winter retreats.

Today, the migration of birds commands an immense amount of interest and the literature on the subject is almost overwhelming. All that I can hope to attempt here is to outline some of the essential features of the phenomenon.

Several problems have yet to be answered satisfactorily. For instance, why does a bird first forsake the region in which it was born? What determines the direction and extent of its outward journey? Why does it ever return to the breeding territory and how does it retrace its path?

Artificial extension of daylight in the autumn has been shown to cause the reproductive organs to ripen earlier than usual, but castrated crows are ready to migrate at the normal time. Anyhow, young birds migrate too, and usually before their parents into the bargain. So the phenomenon cannot be related entirely to reproduction.

Bird migration does not always take place by means of flight. Penguins migrate from the pack ice on which they pass the winter to the Antarctic continent for breeding. Migratory guillemots mostly swim and the American coot walks for miles across country.

It has been found that, in most cases, birds tend to breed in the coldest part of their range. This may be associated with abundant food in the breeding area during the spring. Migration involves a gradual change in the area occupied by a species: it is not to be compared with the despatch of a vast army to foreign shores. There is close relationship with weather conditions, but migration is more regular than the seasons because it is controlled by the effect of day-length on the pituitary gland. Thus in 1931, many swallows were caught by a cold spell in this country and killed before they were ready to migrate.

Much migration, especially of small song-birds (p. 106), takes place at night when it is not usually observed. Stronger and faster species, however, such as crows and swallows usually travel by day. Migrating birds do not fly at great heights and will descend to low level after crossing a mountain range. Nor do they move particularly fast. They just move steadily and relentlessly onward, now and again stopping to feed. Many call incessantly during flight which is a mechanism for keeping them together (p. 63). Indeed, migration is an immense process which reaches its highest degree in the insectivorous song-birds, cuckoos, swifts, terns and waders. It occurs constantly throughout the year in different parts of the globe. And when one considers that a bird may fly half across the world and back again the same year, then it is easy to realise that it must spend a considerable part of its life on migration.

The complexity of migration is increased by additional factors. Migratory parents may have resident offspring and vice versa; spring migration may take place in a bird which did not migrate the previous autumn; different communities tend to use separate routes. Some birds return to the exact locality each year, others do not. In fact, there seem to be awkward exceptions to every generalisation that can be made.

The significance and advantages of migration are easier to comprehend. It enables birds to avoid excessively hot summers and equally cold winters when food shortage would be a great problem. It has been shown experimentally that small birds can survive deep winter frost in Canada if they are well fed and provided with illumination during the night so that they can see to eat. But they will die of starvation and cold in the course of a single night if left in darkness. The migratory habit also brings birds to areas suitable for breeding and to where there are suitable nesting sites.

Migratory behaviour is instinctive. The primary factor is usually physiological stimulation of the pituitary gland by increasing length of day in the spring and decreasing day-length in autumn, enhanced by climatic changes: but daylight cannot affect birds wintering in the equatorial region. The origin of migration is little understood, although the habit may have evolved at the time of the retreat of the ice age.

What determines the direction of migration is again unknown. It has recently been suggested, however, that birds navigate by means of the sun's arc which is estimated visually. Provided the bird has an exact knowledge of the time of day, the principles used are exactly similar to those employed by mariners. The existence of some form of internal chronometer has now been established beyond doubt, but the nature of the basic rhythmic process which can keep chronometers running for many days when the environmental rhythm has been removed experimentally, remains obscure.

Recently experiments have been carried out into the nocturnal migration of warblers. Even when birds were hatched in completely enclosed, sound-proof chambers in constant light, so that there were no outward clues of the yearly seasonal rhythm, nevertheless in the autumn at the time of migration they would fly restlessly from perch to perch. In the spring they underwent another spell of restless, wakeful nights. When placed in a cage with a glass top, the birds orientated themselves by the stars and fluttered in the normal direction of migration. They were therefore tested for the ability to orientate themselves in a planetarium. By changing the north-south declination (height) of the stars it was possible to change the apparent geographical latitude, making the birds believe that they were farther south or north than they actually were. Similarly by shifting the sky in the east-west direction they could be misled about their position in longitude. In either case the warblers responded in a manner indicating a remarkable hereditary mechanism for astral orientation coupled with precise time-sense. At the very first glimpse of the sky the birds automatically 'know' the right direction but on dark nights with thick cloud they get lost.

One of the driving forces in animal evolution is selection of the environment by the organism; and this is achieved chiefly by migration and emigration. It would not be going too far to say that migration is a key to the elasticity of animal communities and therefore one of the chief tools of natural selection.

Chapter 9

The origin of social behaviour in insects

THE GREAT MAJORITY OF INSECTS, like arachnids, lead solitary lives. Except for the brief period when they are engaged in mating, they disregard each other entirely. Social insects are defined as those in which parents and offspring live together in a common abode. An essential feature, therefore, is the prolongation of the life of the female so that she has cognisance of her young. Locusts, caterpillars, ladybirds and other insects which collect in vast swarms are not social; they are said to be gregarious. This is a temporary phenomenon which does not involve any association of parents and offspring.

Gregarious habits

Some of the most striking instances of gregarious living are found in certain caterpillars. Familar British examples include the larvae of the small tortoiseshell butterfly, *Aglais urticae*, which feed upon nettles in June and August. Gregarious when young, later on they become scattered as they wander away in search of more food. The offspring of the lackey moth, *Malacosoma neustria*, and the small eggar, *Eriogaster lanestris*, spin elaborate silken webs in which to shelter. Such a web may contain several hundred individuals and its size increases as its inhabitants spread themselves further for food. Their communal life continues until the caterpillars are almost mature. Other species with gregarious habits include the small ermine moths, *Hyponomeuta* spp., whose larvae spin dense masses of grey web among the leaves and twigs of spindle trees, and the buff-tip, *Phalera bucephala*. Aggregations of the black-and-yellow striped caterpillars of this insect are often to be seen on lime and other trees in late summer. Many saw-fly larvae are gregarious too. In most instances, such caterpillars are brightly coloured and distasteful, so that they gain protection from their gregarious habits which render them even more conspicuous than they would be if they were solitary.

Some adult insects, also, show gregarious habits. For example, the cluster-fly, *Pollenia rudis*, related to the common blow-fly but clothed in fine, shiny golden hairs, receives the name on account of its habit of hibernating in large aggregations. Favourite retreats for this purpose include lofts, disused rooms and the roofs of churches. Sometimes the same room is invaded year after year, even though it has been redecorated in an effort to deter the insects. It is not known what attracts them, and the mystery is only heightened by the fact that a new generation of flies is involved each year. Presumably some scent or chemical sense is involved for insects are well known to be highly sensitive to odours far outside the range of human perception.

The larvae of the cluster-fly are parasites on the common garden earthworm, *Allolobophora chlorotica*. The female fly deposits her eggs in the soil during the autumn and on hatching the larva penetrates into the coelomic cavity of a worm by way of the genital opening. During the following winter the parasite does not feed, but when the temperature of the soil rises in the spring, it migrates forward until it reaches the anterior end of the worm, when it penetrates the skin and protrudes its post-abdominal spiracles. Having safeguarded respiratory needs, the larva now begins to feed actively, growing quickly as it devours the tissues of its host. Eventually the worm is almost entirely consumed and the parasite buries itself deeply in the soil and forms a puparium from which the adult fly finally emerges. In this case, therefore, gregariousness is not found during larval development.

The common two-spotted ladybird, *Adalia bipunctata*, hibernates in small, closely packed parties and some other species are even more gregarious. In California, the convergent ladybird, *Hippodamia convergens*, feeds on greenfly in coastal districts during the summer, but when autumn comes the beetles move towards the hills and congregate in masses at altitudes of 5,000 feet or more, hidden under stones, dead leaves and in pine woods. At one time the insects were collected in large numbers during the winter and kept in cold storage so that they could be released wherever there was danger of an outbreak of greenfly. This was carried out for several years, but the results were disappointing. The insects collected in their winter sleep had an instinct to migrate on awakening: consequently when they were released on the coast, most of them must have flown off into the Pacific Ocean!

The behaviour of some insects during migration is interesting for they form dense companies, often of great size. These insects include the small and large white butterflies, *Pieris rapae* and *P. brassicae*, which occasionally invade the southern counties of England in vast swarms. Dragonflies, such as *Libellula quadrimaculata*, and hoverflies too, sometimes make long flights gregariously during which they do not hesitate to cross the waters of the sea. On occasions immense numbers have been recorded off Heligoland.

Finally, it might be mentioned that during the mating period, the males of some species of gnats and crane-flies indulge in lively nuptial dances, performing aerial gymnastics as they gyrate in the sunshine. Swarming gnats invariably choose a conspicuous site for their dances and will at once return to it if blown away by a sudden gust of wind.

Gregariousness and social life are not necessarily closely connected in insects although in mammals it is possible to see how one may have led to the other (see p. 127).

Sub-social behaviour

Apart from gregarious behaviour, a number of quite unrelated arthropods show well marked sub-social tendencies. Thus, although spiders and scorpions are fierce, predatory and cannibalistic animals, always ready to devour creatures smaller than themselves, as though to offset their aggressive behaviour many species are endowed with pronounced maternal instincts.

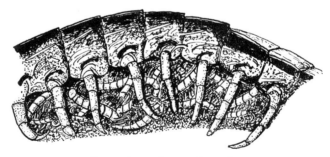

Parental care in a scolopendra

The fertilised eggs of the scorpion develop inside the mother and the young are born alive. In some species the eggs are rich in yolk which the embryos consume during their development. In others, however, the fertilised egg becomes closely commingled with the maternal tissues and as development proceeds a tubular extension like an umbilical cord develops. Along this pass nutrient fluids from the walls of the mother's intestine. These fluids are transformed by glandular secretions and then led to a kind of teat in the baby scorpion's mouth.

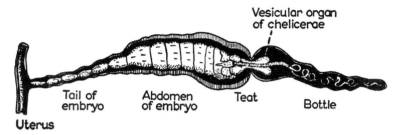

The developing embryos of a scorpion showing bottle and teat (enlarged)

The young scorpions are usually born at night. As soon as they have freed themselves from the membrane that surrounds them, they climb upon their mother's back. This process may take them up to two hours as they are very plump and weak. Once in position, they remain without feeding for a week or more, until their first moult, when they acquire a typical scorpion-like appearance. After this, they do not stay with their mother for more than a day or two longer before they scatter.

Female wolf-spiders carry their egg-sacs about with them until the young have hatched. The baby spiderlings then ride on their mother's back for the first few days of their lives but before long they disperse, for they are greedy creatures. Until mating time comes, they will not again approach one another except with hostile intent. In most species the egg-sac or cocoon is attached to the spinnerets of the mother, but in some she grasps it with her jaws. The cocoon is a rather flattened sphere with an equatorial line around it, giving the effect of two valves. Its removal is strongly resisted by the mother spider who will search for it in all directions if it is taken away.

Although the prey is hunted by sight, the female wolf-spider apparently recognises an egg-sac by feeling it with her pedipalps. To be more accurate of course, one should say that she responds to the tactile stimulation it provides. The cocoon of another spider, even of a different species, is accepted with alacrity provided that it is not greatly dissimilar in size to her own. One spider even accepted an egg-sac in which a leaden shot had been inserted, making it many times its original weight. She could hardly crawl under the burden, but stuck to it gallantly, and when several attempts to secure it to her spinnerets had failed, she carried it about between her jaws and the third pair of legs.

In some web-building spiders, gregarious or sub-social behaviour persists throughout life. For example an Australian species, *Amaurobius socialis*, from the Jenolan Caves constructs enormous communal and densely fabricated webs measuring as much as 12 feet in length and 4 feet in width, which are inhabited by a large number of individuals.

A rudimentary social structure has also been described in certain ticks and other mites which are said to remain with their eggs and defend them if disturbed.

A recently discovered species of mite, *Myrmonyssus phalae-nodectes*, however, provides an example of somewhat more elaborate social behaviour. This animal is a widely distributed parasite in the auditory organs of moths of the family Noctuidae. The fully developed, engorged female is a yellow mite about a half-milli-metre in length: the male is somewhat smaller, with shorter and stouter legs. Both sexes live together in colonies destroying the function of one of its host's ears; the other ear is always left undamaged. In an experiment, nine mites were placed in various positions on a single moth. Within a short while they had established themselves as a single colony in the moth's right ear, and even when this later became quite uninhabitable as a result of a mould, and the mites were swarming all over the head and thorax of the host, the remaining tympanic organ was unharmed.

When an intruding mite attempts to enter an occupied ear it is jostled and repulsed by the mites already established there, but even so will not enter the uninhabited ear of the host. It is almost as though the mites realised that if they were to make the moth deaf in both ears, it would be unable to detect the high pitched squeaks of bats so that both it and its parasites would be exposed to early extinction!

It has been shown experimentally that the initial choice of ear by the first mite is quite random, but that succeeding mites will always enter the same orifice. The mechanism by which this is achieved is not yet understood but it is clear that the mite colony represents something more than a mere chance aggregation and contains the rudiments of a true society.

In a similar way, when a number of false-scorpions are obtaining free transport by attaching themselves to a fly, a habit that is not uncommon amongst the group, they invariably do so in such a way as not to unbalance their host.

Sub-social habits are found in species belonging to a number of different groups of insects. In each of these, therefore, a separate and independent attempt to forsake a purely solitary mode of life has taken place. In most cases only the beginnings of social organisation appear, but even so, some of the essential features that characterise the highest expression of social behaviour are foreshadowed.

The earwig, for instance, deposits her eggs in an excavation that she has previously prepared below the surface of the soil and she remains on guard over them as well as over the young for a short time after they have hatched. Mole-crickets also dig underground chambers in which the eggs are deposited. Some pentatomid bugs lay a batch of about 30 eggs over which the female stands. If chased away, she at once returns to them. By so doing she protects them to some extent from egg-parasites, for often the eggs on the circumference of the batch, which are incompletely covered by her body, are the only ones to be attacked. The young nymphs remain with their mother for several days after hatching.

Among beetles, the scarab, *Scarabaeus sacer*, shows the beginnings of sub-social behaviour. This insect acts as a scavenger by breaking up and burying the droppings of cattle and other animals.

The scarab beetle, *Scarabaeus sacer* (length about 1½ ins)

The female detaches a portion of dung and forms it into a pellet, sometimes as large as a fist, and compacts this by pushing it backwards uphill with her hind legs and allowing it to roll down again. The ball is then rolled away by the beetle, who pushes when necessary with her broad head, or walks backwards, dragging it along with her front legs.

Not infrequently she is assisted by a 'friend', who is usually of the same sex, until a suitable place is reached and the owner commences to excavate a chamber for the reception of her prize. Sometimes her helpmate takes this opportunity to roll the ball off for her own use; but if no such mishap occurs, the *Scarabaeus* buries it in a subterranean chamber and remains with it until the food is entirely exhausted, when a fresh supply is sought.

In the autumn, a larger subterranean chamber is found, to which the beetle carries dung until it has accumulated a large mass of provender in which an egg is deposited. In certain other dung-beetles, such as *Copris hispanus* and *C. lunaris*, the male and female combine to excavate a very much larger earth chamber to contain from two to seven ellipsoidal balls of dung, in each of which an egg is laid. These are guarded while the larvae are devouring the food thus provided and when the young beetles emerge they are escorted to the exterior and the little family disperses. The devotion of the parent beetles may well be the origin of the charming Arabic proverb: 'In the eyes of a mother dung-beetle her young are as the gazelle'! There are a number of other dung-beetles which exhibit very similar parental behaviour, more or less well developed.

Probably because of the obvious disadvantages of marine life, which include tides, waves, salinity and deficiency of calcium salts, the only part of the globe that has not to any great degree been exploited by insects is the shore and the waters of the ocean. In the tidal zone and in salt marshes, the life of terrestrial insects is governed by few, but very extreme environmental factors: consequently any behaviour which provides elaborate care of the progeny, even at the expense of some reduction in reproductive capacity, will benefit the population.

Staphylinid beetles of the genus *Bledius* which inhabit sandy beaches and salt-marshes where they are covered daily by the tide, take special care of their eggs. In some species the mother makes a nest tunnel in which she and her mate dwell. In the walls she digs rooms for her eggs and the newly hatched larvae live in the nest and eat algae collected by their parents. Sometimes the male and

PLATE XIII

Termites at work

PLATE XIV

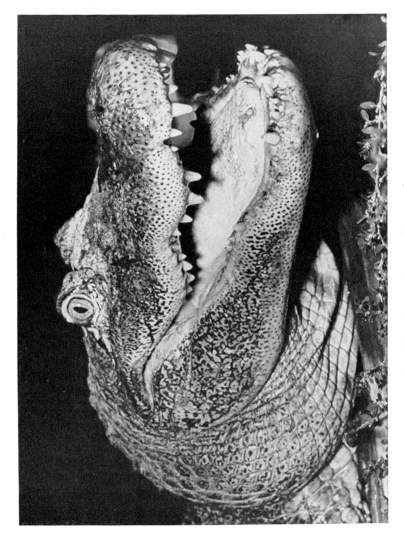

Crocodiles show a degree of parental care

PLATE XV

Catfish family

PLATE XVI

Mother and young at water-hole

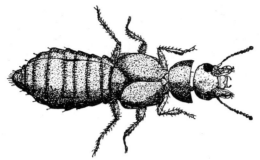

The subsocial beetle, *Bledius* sp. (length about 3 mm)

female defend the entrance of the nest against intruders, but the highly specialised family behaviour seems mainly to be a protection against extreme physical conditions.

A slight advance in social behaviour can be seen in some species of the interesting little insects known as 'web-spinners' which comprise the order Embioptera, found in most tropical and sub-tropical countries. Some species are purely solitary and live under bark and stones or in hollow grass stems. The Himalayan *Embia major*, inhabits dense silken tunnels which it constructs beneath stones. The female lives in close association with her eggs and young, protecting them with her body. As the young grow older they show a tendency to wander off and construct adjacent tunnels for themselves. The whole colony is social in tendency and as many as

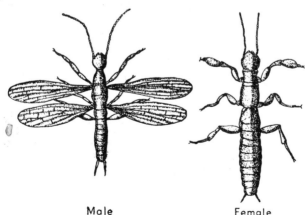

Male   Female
Tropical web-spinners (Embioptera) (length about
1 inch)

115

twenty-one adult insects have been found inhabiting a compound nest of interlacing passages.

The West Indian species, *Clothoda urichi*, constructs silken webs as tunnels on the bark of tree trunks. In these live several males and females with their offspring. The webs often cover a large area on a tree trunk, for they are tough and resistant to the weather and remain long after they have been abandoned. The silk is secreted by a number of small glands on the enlarged first tarsal segments of the front pair of legs. Whilst the insect is spinning, these legs are waved quickly from side to side.

Characteristics of social behaviour

True social life has developed only in two orders of insects. These are the Isoptera, or termites, and the Hymenoptera which includes ants, bees and wasps. The termites, sometimes called 'white ants', are a lowly archaic group more closely related to cockroaches than to any other insects. They show gradual metamorphosis and there is no larval or pupal stage of development. The Hymenoptera, on the other hand, rank amongst the most highly specialised of all insects. It is remarkable, therefore, that the evolutionary plan moulding the social life of these divergent groups has pursued paths that run so nearly parallel.

Although social behaviour is innate, neverthless a greater degree of plasticity and modifiability is found than in the reflex actions of non-social insects. A good memory and time-sense are required, especially in bees which visit different crops at the time of nectar-flow. Other characteristics of social behaviour include highly sensitive smell-recognition for intercommunication, specialised reproduction with the development of sterile 'castes', and finally *'trophallaxis'* the mutual exchange of food between members of the colony.

It is among the wasps that the evolution of social organisation in the Hymenoptera can best be seen. In the next chapter the social life of ants and bees will be considered. The termites are left until last, because the phases of social organisation displayed among them can best be appreciated in relation to those prevailing in the Hymenoptera.

Sub-social behaviour in wasps

The structure and behaviour of the more primitive wasp families indicate that from them arose the ancestors of both the bees and the ants. Many species are quite solitary but others show traces of social behaviour. Solitary hunting-wasps paralyse or kill their prey by means of the ovipositor which has become modified as a sting. The prey, which may be a spider, a caterpillar or some other insect, is stored in a nest and an egg is laid on it. When this hatches, the larva or grub feeds upon the paralysed victim.

The nest-making solitary wasps can be divided into three main groups. The least advanced are spider-hunters which first catch and paralyse a spider, then hide it and look for a nesting site. This means that the position of the single cell has to be remembered for a short time only. The sand-wasps build their nests, which consist of long, branched tunnels, before they seek their prey, which may be any kind of insect or spider. When several paralysed creatures have been stored, an egg is laid and the cell sealed up. Thus the

Hunting-wasp dragging a hawk-moth caterpillar to her burrow

mother has no contact with her young although she must become very familiar with the surroundings of the nest since many cells are constructed in the same spot. The third group includes the eumenid wasps which build nests like those of sand-wasps: but they do not bring food to the cell until the egg has hatched. In this way the mother has some contact with her young. In certain African species, the female may feed her offspring with chewed fragments of prey instead of whole specimens.

Social wasps

Social wasps produce annual colonies in temperate regions, perennial colonies in the tropics. There are two sorts of females, egg-laying queens and workers. Males occur for a short period at the end of the summer when they fertilise the young queens of the next generation. The workers are not quite sterile because some of them may lay eggs, especially if the queen dies; but these un-fertilised eggs produce only males so that the workers alone could not carry on the species.

The young queen hibernates throughout the winter. In the spring she constructs a small nest of not more than 10–20 cells, for when the larvae are growing actively it is all that she can do to feed this number without any assistance. Up till now, her behaviour is similar to that of a solitary wasp showing progressive provisioning of her nest, but when the first workers emerge from the cocoon, a real social unit has started. The young workers at once take over tasks of nest construction and feeding the developing larvae: before long the queen performs no duties other than egg laying. Eventually she loses all powers of flight.

Divisions of labour, such a feature of the '*caste*' system of ants and termites, is not so marked in wasps. On the other hand trophal-laxis is: adult wasps engaged on feeding the grub eagerly lick up the secretion produced by the labial glands. For whereas wasp larvae are carnivorous and are fed by the workers on insects chewed into a paste, adult wasps can swallow only liquid food such as nectar, fruit juice and jam.

It has been suggested that trophallaxis in wasps has a direct bearing upon the origin of the worker caste. On account of the ex-penditure of saliva by the larvae and the numbers reared simul-taneously, many are inadequately nourished and pupate as small individuals which emerge with imperfectly developed reproductive organs. Furthermore the labour of tending the ravenous brood tends to keep the workers sterile. Only later in the season does an abundance of food and of worker wasps permit the larvae to be more copiously fed. Many therefore develop into fertile male-producing individuals, others become the future queens whose eggs are fertilised and produce females.

The wasp larva cannot foul its cell because its crop does not communicate with the hind-gut until the final instar or stage in larval development. Waste products in the form of insoluble uric acid crystals (p. 30) are secreted only once, just before pupation.

Chapter 10

The world of ants and bees

The hive contained one obstinate bee
(His name was Peter), and thus spake he —
'Though every bee has shown white feather,
To bow to tyranny I'm not prone —
Why should a hive swarm all together?
Surely a bee can swarm alone?'
W. S. GILBERT (1867)

FEW INSECTS are more familiar than the honey-bee which has been exploited by man since the dawn of civilisation. A cave painting at Araña, in Spain, gives a vivid impression of a Palaeolithic man climbing down a rope-ladder to collect honey from a nest of wild bees on a rocky cliff. Nevertheless, the majority of bees are inconspicuous, solitary species. It is probable that they have evolved from the same ancestors as the sand-wasps, the beginning of the divergence being a change in habit from hunting to collecting vegetable food. Some tropical wasps live entirely on nectar and pollen. Bees do the same, but they have developed branched hairs which entangle pollen grains and enable a larger load to be carried.

As well as losing the primitive carnivorous habit, bees show a second refinement over wasps in that the comb is built with wax and not 'wasp paper' composed of chewed wood fibres.

Bumble-bees

It is well-known that the visits of bees benefit flowers by transferring pollen from one to another. Mice are said to destroy the nests of bumble-bees so that if cats are about to kill the mice, more clover-seed will set. Deep in the ground, bumble-bees build an irregular nest of grass or moss fragments formed into a hollow ball; while certain species, known as 'carder-bees' construct surface nests among the ground herbage.

The social organisation of the bumble-bees resembles that of social wasps. In temperate regions the colony is an annual one, founded by a single fertilised queen who comes out of hibernation on the advent of mild weather in the spring. After constructing a nest, she accumulates a paste-like mass of pollen and nectar. On this she places a cell of wax containing a batch of eggs. She also makes a number of receptacles which she fills with honey.

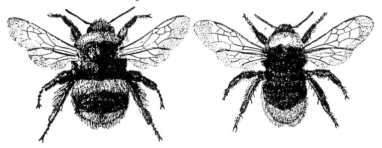

A queen and her 'cuckoo'. Left, queen bumble-bee, *Bombus terrestris*; right, female 'cuckoo' bumble-bee, *Psithyrus vestalis*

When the larvae first hatch they feed on the pollen paste the queen has prepared for them; but later she gnaws a hole in the roof of the cell and regularly supplies her brood with regurgitated honey and pollen. After about three weeks the first workers emerge. Additional cells are then formed until the colony increases to a maximum of about 500 bees. Later in the season, queens and males are produced. After fertilisation which, in many species, takes place in June or July, the young queens go into hibernation and the remainder of the colony breaks up.

Honey-bees

Food sharing or trophallaxis is the basis of communication in the honey-bee colony since it is associated with the production of distinctive odours, and so with the recognition of companions and the defence of the colony. It enables worker bees to be apprised of the presence of the queen so that, in the event of any deficiency, another is raised. It also enables new foragers to learn about suitable crops and helps to ensure an effective division of labour in the hive.

The various castes, queen, drone and worker are more clearly differentiated than in any of the social wasps and the various duties of the workers are generally apportioned according to their age. At first they are engaged in cleaning the broodcells and in keeping the brood warm. From the third to the sixth day they feed the older larvae and then they devote their attentions to the younger grubs and the queen. After the fourteenth day of adult life they spend their time secreting wax, comb-building and cleaning the hive. Between the eighteenth and twentieth days they guard the entrance of the hive after which they become foragers for the rest of their existence. The average length of life of an adult worker hive-bee is about forty days.

One of the most fascinating aspects of bee behaviour is the method by which one forager can by dancing communicate to others the locality of a rich source of nectar. If the food is near the hive the so-called 'round dance' is employed; if more than a hundred metres a 'tail-wagging dance'. The intensity of dancing varies with the richness of the newly discovered food source. The scent brought back by the dancing bee indicates to her companions the type of flower to be visited while the direction of the dance

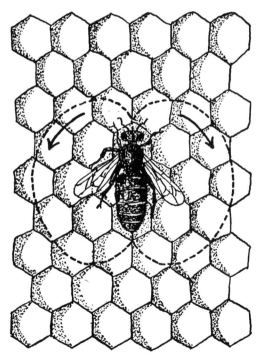

The language of honey-bees

from the vertical on the comb indicates the angle of the food from the direction of the sun. If the sun is obscured by cloud, polarisation of the light in the sky gives a direction of reference.

I must confess that when I first read about the language of the bees I could hardly bring myself to believe it! Only when I realised that it is merely an extension within the hive of the 'light-compass orientation' found in other insects, could I rationalise the phenomenon to my satisfaction.

It has long been known that marching locusts keep direction by maintaining a constant angle between their path and the direction of the sun. They can be thrown into confusion by a mirror reflecting the sun's rays from a new direction: some continue on the old course while others turn to maintain the original angle, but with the sun's reflection in the mirror. In a similar way foraging ants will return to the nest, steering by the angle of the sun. Now, inside the hive the sun's position is represented by the vertical and the dance merely orientates the source of food from this reference point rather than from the actual position of the sun which, of course, the bees cannot see while they are inside. If an insect flies at a fixed angle to the sun, its direction will change slowly during the day, unless it is able to allow for the change in angle necessitated by the apparent solar movement. Bees normally have some internal 'clock' system to offset this: but the nature of this physiological chronometer is quite unknown. It may be similar to that found in birds (p. 106).

Bee colonies are perennial, but surplus drones are pushed out of the hive (not stung to death as is often supposed) before the winter. In tropical regions the activities of the hive are determined by the alternation of rainy and dry seasons, for comparatively little honey is produced during wet weather.

When the hive gets too hot, the bees cool it by bringing in water which is deposited on the upper parts of the combs. Then they fan vigorously with their wings and drive the air cooled by evaporation through the brood comb. On the other hand, in winter, the workers can warm the hive when necessary by running about and generally undergoing physical exercise. This increases the rate of metabolism so that their bodies are warmed.

Ants

Social behaviour reaches its highest development in ants and there are no solitary species. Different species construct very diverse kinds of nests: some consist of underground chambers and galleries, others of heaps of pine-needles and other vegetable matter. Perhaps the most usual consist of hollows in the ground beneath stones and logs which serve as protective coverings.

The 'legionary' or 'driver' ants of tropical regions do not construct permanent nests, but lead a nomadic life, occasionally halting to build temporary bivouacs. Like other primitive ants, they are carnivorous, but none rival them in ferocity. These dreaded creatures, blind but with well-developed powers of scent, roam the

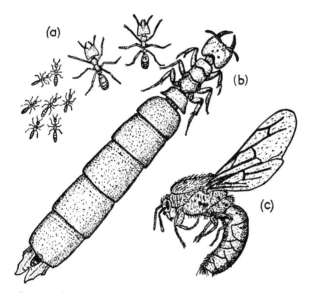

Castes of an African driver ant, *Dorylus* sp., drawn under the same magnification (*a*) workers, (*b*) queen, (*c*) male

country in huge bands, devouring any living creature which does not take to flight. The giant python sleeping after a heavy meal is reduced to a skeleton within a few minutes and woe betide the imperial scorpion who crosses their path, for he certainly cannot run fast enough to escape! Only the giant black millipede is sufficiently distasteful to be safe from their murderous attentions.

Among the higher ants, many genera have turned from hunting and taken to a pastoral existence, living directly or indirectly on the sap of plants. In some cases this 'honey-dew' is secreted by plants in special nectaries, the plant obtaining protection from its association with the ants. More often, however, ants exploit the surplus sugary waste matter produced by aphids and other plant-sucking bugs. (The wasteful feeding habits of these insects are due to the fact that plant sap contains very little nitrogen, so they are forced to consume enormous quantities in order to obtain sufficient protein for their needs.)

In some ant species, the pastoral stage has given way to agriculture. 'Harvester ants' collect the seeds of grasses and store them

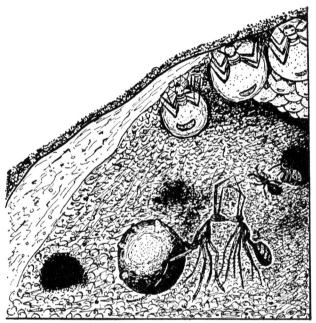

Honey-pot ants in their underground store-cellar
(enlarged)

in underground granaries, while the leaf-cutting ants, common in the tropics of the New World, use the vegetable matter they collect so destructively to form a compost heap. On this they grow fungi for food and tend their plots as assiduously as any human gardener

Whereas bees store liquid food in the honey-comb, ants use some of their own workers as honey-pots. '*Repletes*' as these are called, have an enormously distensible crop. They are incapable of walking, but remain suspended from the ceiling of underground chambers in the nest. In time of plenty they are filled with food collected and regurgitated by the foragers, until their abdomens are completely spherical and several times the normal size. Then, in the dry season they provide for the entire colony from their capacious bellies.

Ants are among the few animals, other than man, which go to war in armies. Some ants, such as the legionaries, are merely predatory, but slave-makers invade the nests of other species to steal pupae. Sometimes they meet with easy success, at others with violent resistance. After the battle, the returning column, loaded with booty, follows the precise route that it took on the outward journey, for the slave-makers are guided solely by smell.

Termites

Though termites are quite unrelated to ants, their social behaviour affords many interesting parallels. All the species are social but there are several fundamental distinctions between the organisation of the Isoptera and that of Hymenoptera. In the first place, the colony is always founded by a 'royal' pair instead of by a solitary queen. Secondly the workers, soldiers and non-reproductive castes comprise both sexes in approximately equal numbers, so that males have social importance instead of merely reproductive functions. More castes are found among termites than among other social insects.

In the majority of species, except the most primitive, there are at least ten different castes; these are reproductive, workers and soldiers, each represented by both sexes. Soldiers are frequently of

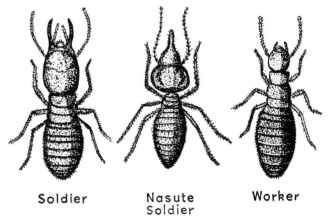

Soldier   Nasute   Worker
              Soldier

The non-reproductive castes of termites (enlarged)

125

two kinds, '*mandibulate*' and '*nasute*'. In the latter, the large jaws of the mandibulate soldier are replaced by vestigial mandibles and the retort-shaped head is drawn out into a rostrum. This bears at its apex the opening of a large gland which secretes an adhesive liquid used in defence of the colony. Both workers and soldiers may be differentiated into sub-castes, differing, just as in ants, in the size and proportions of head and body.

Termites are pre-eminently eaters of wood, but some of the more advanced species eat other vegetable matter also. As in the Hymenoptera, trophallaxis is the bond governing social behaviour. Just as honey-bees eagerly lick the body of their queen, thereby obtaining the 'queen substance' which plays such a vital part in the economy of the hive; so do termite workers lick up the exudations secreted from the distended bodies of their gross queens.

Social parasites

The very success of social insects has led to their exploitation by hordes of other creatures. Not infrequently a solitary species such as the 'cuckoo-bee', *Psithyrus rupestris*, becomes the social parasite or '*inquiline*' of a related but social species, in this case the bumble-bee, *Bombus lapidarius*. In the spring a female *Psithyrus* enters the nest of a bumble-bee and stings the host queen to death. After this her own eggs and young are cared for by the remaining bumble-bee workers as faithfully as if they were the offspring of the rightful queen. Even the members of non-parasitic species fight for suitable nesting sites. It is quite possible, therefore, that the parasitic habit may have arisen in species that tended to leave hibernation somewhat late in the spring, so that the host species had already established its nests before it was attacked. A similar phenomenon occurs in wasps.

The relations between ant communities of different species vary. In some cases two species may occupy a compound nest, in others one species reduces the other to slavery. In termites too, there occur all stages between amicable association and outright parasitism.

In addition to the other social insects, the nests of ants and termites especially, harbour a weird assortment of spiders, centipedes, millipedes, woodlice, false-scorpions, silverfish, beetles, flies and other insects which gain food, shelter and more equable conditions than prevail outside. In many cases these 'guests' are welcomed because they possess special glands providing aromatic secretions on which the ants feed. But some 'guests' are decidedly anti-social for they eat the larvae of the ants and provide very little in return.

The development of social behaviour in higher animals

Social co-operation in animals usually begins with mutual attraction. Individuals do not just stumble upon each other but approach, often from great distances, as when male moths assemble round a female or birds migrate to a breeding area independently. Once they come together, however, in pairs or in groups, one sees several degrees of co-operation. One of the simplest consists in all the animals doing the same thing. When one bird is frightened, all fly away. If hens that have just satisfied their hunger see one of their number beginning to eat again, they all join in. In a similar way when we yawn we make others do so; and it is well known that fear is catching. When an allied infantry regiment was beginning to break at one stage during the Great War, the splendid sight of a squadron of British cavalry trotting towards the front was sufficient to enable them to recover their shattered morale.

All birds and mammals whose young are born in a helpless state are, to some degree social. Often, too, there is a division of

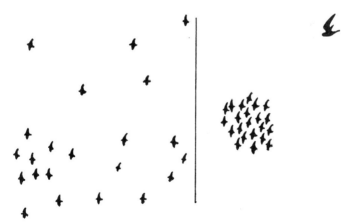

Advantages of group activity. Left, flock of starlings undisturbed. Right, their reaction to a peregrine falcon. The peregrine can only catch a flying bird by swooping down at an enormous speed which makes it vulnerable to collisions. Therefore it cannot attack birds in a dense flock

labour. The male kestrel brings food to the nest, but does not himself feed the young. He hands the prey to his mate who then gives it to the babies. The male hornbill walls up the female in the hollow tree in which the birds have built their nest, leaving only a tiny hole through which he feeds her. Division of labour is carried to its ultimate extreme among the social insects we have been discussing.

From the simplest courtship and mating responses, social cooperation extends to care of the young. A third stage is the development of the social group from family life, which finds its highest fulfilment in human societies.

Ants and men

The problems raised by social behaviour in animals have certain aspects in common, but here any similarity between insect and human societies begins and ends. The solutions to these difficulties have been achieved in each case by entirely different methods. Perhaps the most pressing need is for some method of controlling reproduction in social animals whose offspring have enhanced chances of survival.

Most social mammals have a restricted breeding season which tends to limit their numbers: at other times of the year the relations between the sexes are platonic. Man is one of the few animals capable of breeding at any season. In the past, the regulation of human populations has been achieved mainly by disease and marriage customs that reduce promiscuity. When the mortality rate in Western Europe began to decline at the beginning of the nineteenth century, exploitation of the New World provided a new source of food and the invention of railway engines and steamships provided a means of transporting it to the increasing millions. But agricultural expansion cannot continue indefinitely and human population control remains the great problem of the future.

Social insects have solved the difficulty by the production of neuter castes. In termites, the sterilisation of most individuals of each sex must have occurred early in the history of the group. Ants, bees and wasps on the other hand, have a form of sex-determination which enables purely female broods to be produced over long periods: unfertilised eggs beget male offspring and fertilisation is under nervous control. In addition, surplus eggs and larvae are eaten.

A second problem is that hunting does not produce a supply of food sufficiently large and regular to permit of many animals living in the same place. In man, large communities only developed with the advent of agriculture; in ants with the exploitation of vegetable foods, greenfly 'cattle' and so on. Driver ants only maintain large hunting colonies at the expense of being permanently nomadic.

Finally, among insects a stable community depends upon the greatly extended life of the queen, so that there is a wide overlap between successive generations; for the queen stabilises the whole system by her oviposition. In man the parents need survive only until the young are self-supporting. But whereas in insects social behaviour is almost entirely instinctive, in man it develops through crafts and traditions, for the learning and development of which a long childhood and a long adult life are required. It should be pointed out, however, that compared with other insects, the social species show an unusually high degree of memory and plasticity in their behaviour. It is in comparison with mammals that their social habits appear to be so stereotyped.

In insects, the fixed, instinctive actions of the daily life are numerous and not at all widely spaced, and only a little latitude is permitted. There are no 'obstinate bees'! In man, on the other hand, between instinctive acts such as feeding and sleeping, there is plenty of opportunity for the individual to indulge in activities in the ethology of which insight and learning play the driving part.

Chapter 11

Family life in birds and mammals

F OR TWELVE YEARS, 'Faith' was the church cat of St. Augustine and St. Faith under St. Paul's. She arrived in 1936 as a stray and the Rector took her into his home adjoining the church. 'Her behaviour during the services was always exemplary, and she sat with great dignity in the pews and choir stalls or, in winter, near the radiators, with her good friend the vergeress.'

In the autumn of 1940, 'Faith' had a kitten which she shielded in a corner of the rectory throughout the air-raids of September 9th. In the words of the tablet recording her bravery during the Battle of Britain: 'Roofs and masonry fell asunder, and the whole house blazed. Four floors fell through in front of "Faith"; fire and water and ruin were all round her. Yet she stayed calm and steadfast and waited for help. We rescued her in the early morning while the place was still burning and by the mercy of God she and her kitten were not only saved but unhurt.'

In the last chapter we discussed the high degree of social behaviour that has been achieved by insects. This depends upon inborn instincts and very little learning is required. Much of the behaviour of birds and mammals can also be explained in terms of instinct. The charming, but anthropomorphic account of 'Faith' the church cat, quoted above, provides an example of an altruistic, social instinct to protect the young triumphing over that of self-preservation.

A large part of a bird's behaviour springs from within, not only in reflex response to physiological urgencies but also in obedience to timing mechanisms which are essentially arbitrary. For example, song phrases are sung at regular, innate intervals. In the spring, the wren divides her time between sitting on her eggs and other activities. Her diurnal rhythm can be split up into a number of sessions and recesses. The lower the temperature, the more time she spends on her eggs, as might be expected, but the sum of the session and the following recess are not affected. Thus the environment has but a secondary, modifying effect upon an inherent activity rhythm. Every twenty minutes or so, some kind of 'physiological alarm clock', similar, perhaps, to that of the lug-worm (p. 25) goes off inside the wren, and she leaves her eggs. The colder it is, the sooner she comes back. Later in the season, when she is feeding her young, another rhythm appears. The frequency with which she visits the nest now shows a well-marked peak every four or five hours.

In the higher animals, instincts are nevertheless more flexible and tend to be more generalised than in insects. Instinctive acts of primary importance to the individual are less rigid and more subject to modifications under pressure from the environment than are behaviour patterns such as those concerned with reproduction which is vital to the species. Especially in mammals, they are supplemented to a greater or lesser degree by activities that are learned. In man, where learning is exceptionally well-developed and instinct correspondingly less important, a very long period of childhood is necessary.

In all animals, learning and innate behaviour patterns are complementary to one another. Differences in specific behaviour represent differences of degree rather than of kind, although learning plays a minor rôle among invertebrates. Young birds make flight movements long before they are old enough to leave the nest, but if they are prevented from so doing, their ability to fly is in no way retarded. On the other hand, squirrels become expert at cracking nuts by first gnawing a groove round the circumference of the shell. If they are prevented from practising this, they never achieve success although both elements of the complete behaviour pattern are innate. Herring gulls instinctively break cockle shells by dropping their prey from a height. Although they can learn to fly along particular routes where they obtain maximum benefit from uprising air currents, they never learn to select a hard surface on which to drop their cockles, a trick which crows learn very quickly.

As a general rule, birds of both sexes share nesting duties, but in greatly varying proportions. In the more primitive species both sexes take part in incubation as well as in the care of the young, but in species of more advanced taxonomic rank the male commonly does not brood although he still helps to bring food to the young and in some cases feeds the female too.

A common characteristic of reproductive behaviour patterns is the gradual way in which they develop and then recede during the yearly cycle. It is probable that incubation attentiveness is initiated by hormones, but it may also require a tactile stimulus from a full set of eggs. The amount of incubation that the first eggs receive before the later ones are laid affects their intervals of hatching, but once incubation is well established it tends to remain more or less uniform until the young hatch, although affected by air temperature. Brooding tends to decrease during the day until early or mid-afternoon and rises again in the evening. This rhythm is especially pronounced in warm weather and is scarcely noticeable during a cold spell.

Parental care

Parental care occurs in many lower animals, as well as in social insects, fishes, amphibians and reptiles, but it is usually limited to protection of the eggs and young by the parents. In many ways fishes are intermediate between the invertebrates (excluding terrestrial forms) on the one hand, and the remaining vertebrates on the other. Much of their behaviour is instinctive yet they have a typical vertebrate hollow dorsal nerve cord and are capable of a higher degree of learning than is found among invertebrates with the exception of octopuses, cuttlefish and squids.

Fish also show all grades of parental behaviour from random spawning to internal fertilisation, from oviparity to viviparity and from the deposition of a large number of uncared for eggs, to the care of but few. For instance, the cod whose eggs are scattered at random in the open sea, produces over nine million of them; the carp lays from two to four million — again at random but in fresh water and in the neighbourhood of vegetation. The plaice spawns at a depth of 30–40 metres and produces only 300,000 eggs, the sunfish excavates a nest and lays 5,000. Finally, the male stickle-back builds a nest and guards the eggs of which the female produces only 250, while the viviparous dogfish may produce as few as 50–60 offspring.

In some species the males play a relatively passive rôle in the protection of the eggs, but the more active it is, the more its duties seem to be linked with belligerence, a definite courtship and the assumption of conspicuous coloration during the breeding season.

Shannies and gobies are well known for the assiduous way in which they guard the eggs. The gunnel rolls them into a ball and curls round it, both male and female taking part in these duties, whilst the male lumpsucker guards the eggs at considerable risk to

Butterfish, *Pholas gunnellis*, coiling round its eggs

himself both from violent wave action and the activities of predators such as birds and crabs.

Many tropical fishes, such as the Egyptian *Paratilapia multicolor*, guard their babies in their mouths. The male sea-horse,

Male sea-horse showing brood pouch

however, has a brood pouch into which the eggs are laid. After fertilisation they become embedded in the folds of the wall of the pouch and it is believed that a sort of placenta is formed. Certainly an exchange of oxygen and carbon dioxide must take place, since the pouch closes completely during the period of development. When the babies are ready to leave, however, its mouth opens once more and the young sea-horses are ejected by a series of convulsive jerks.

Varying degrees of brood care are to be found among the Amphibia as among fishes. Some species of tree-frog construct mud basins, others use beeswax to seal up pools in tree stumps.

Parental care in Amphibia. Left, male midwife toad carrying eggs; right, female *Pipa americana* showing the receptacles on her back in which the eggs develop

Some construct nests of foam or stick the edges of leaves together to make receptacles for the development of the young; others are viviparous. Parental care is not confined to one sex. In some species the male winds a string of eggs around his legs; in *Rhinoderma darwini* he keeps the eggs in his gular sac which may become so distended that it reaches back as far as the groin, but in others such as *Nototrema marsupeata* and *Pipa americana* the female carries the eggs around until they have developed. In general, amphibians are creatures of instinct and although toads show greater learning ability than frogs, newts or salamanders, they are far from intelligent creatures.

Parental care among reptiles is usually limited in extent. In alligators and crocodiles, however, we see further stages in the association of the family. The eggs of the alligator are incubated in a nest of grass which becomes baked hard by the sun. When the mother hears the cries of her young as they are about to hatch, she digs them out. In the case of the Nile crocodile, the family keep together for a period of about four to twelve months after hatching. The mother also leads the way to the water, constantly uttering a cry which has been described as a 'sucking-like umph'.

In birds and mammals where the parents provide not only food but also shelter and defence against predators, these activities are all accurately timed and are synchronised by means of sign-stimuli. It must be remembered that every ceremony involving the use of signals renders the performing individual conspicuous and therefore vulnerable to enemies. Hence ceremonies have been evolved only where their advantages outweigh their disadvantages.

Although a herring gull cannot recognise one egg from another, it will not incubate an egg placed in its territory before it has laid a clutch of its own. Thus, although the egg provides visual and tactile stimuli that release the brooding reaction, the presence of an internal factor, probably the pituitary hormone 'prolactin', is also necessary. During the first stages of incubation the parent gull will not accept a 'pipped' egg or a very young bird, but later these may be accepted even before its own eggs have reached a similar stage of development. Here 'prolactin' is again necessary for the behaviour reaction, but some other internal factor must also be present. The requisite external sign-stimuli are afforded by the newly born young themselves, or by the sound of their 'peeping' before hatching.

In the case of the stickleback, if the new-laid eggs are exchanged for older ones, the male will accept and guard his apparently premature young. The instinctive 'fanning' reaction in which he circulates water through the nest with his fins is reduced, but reaches a new peak of intensity at the time when the original eggs should have hatched.

Young birds, by gaping, stimulate their parents to feed them. The yellow lining of their mouths, as has already been mentioned, acts as a releaser for the instinctive behaviour pattern. If the young fail to gape, the parent birds look round as though somewhat bewildered and then try to stimulate the babies by touching them and uttering soft cries. If even this fails, the food is usually swallowed by the parent.

Young cuckoos are fed by their foster-parents as they gape greedily while the true offspring or eggs, ejected by the cuckoo, are ignored because they do not provide the correct stimulus. In all species the young one that begs most is fed most and weaklings may be starved to death. I once picked up a baby sparrow which had

Young thrushes gaping

fallen from its nest and placed it conspicuously on a fence. Not only its parents, but apparently most of the adult sparrow population of the neighbourhood came to feed the greedy youngster, for none could resist its pathetic gaping beak!

Not only do parent birds react to their young, but the latter also

Night heron at rest, and performing the 'appeasement ceremony' (right)

react to the adults. The necessity for this is obvious. If every kind of display or advertisement is dangerous to the defenceless young, it is advantageous to them to restrict their begging time to a minimum — that is, to when the parents are actually present to respond. Thus young thrushes begin to gape when their nest is shaken by the adult alighting on it and herring gull chicks are stimulated by their parents 'mew call'. After a few days the chicks learn to recognise their own parents and do not respond to the calls of other adults.

When a night heron comes to the nest, it bows towards the inhabitants whether these be its mate or its young, thereby displaying its blue-black cap and three white plumes which are folded together when at rest. After this introduction it is received cordially and is not attacked by the inmates of the nest.

Nest-relief ceremony by the gentoo penguin

The alarm call of a parent bird inhibits the begging reaction of the young. Baby herring gulls crouch motionless when they hear a warning cry while older chicks run to special refuges near the nest.

Many species of birds have special nest-relief ceremonies. In the herring gull these take the form of a 'mew call' or the presentation of nesting material to the mate. As the young grow up, they begin to assume the appearance of the adult bird which tends to stimulate aggressive behaviour in the parents. This in turn is counteracted, however, by the adoption of a submissive attitude similar to that of the female during courtship which normally inhibits the aggression by the male.

Family life in birds is thus regulated largely by instinctive behaviour. This is much less marked in mammals. If a rat's nest is damaged, the mother will carry her young to a place of safety and build a new nest for them. A mother weasel will do the same. If the young are removed, she will search for them and bring them back when she finds them. At first the rat is somewhat clumsy in her behaviour, but soon she improves by learning and becomes much more gentle with her babies. This learning is associated with the cortex of the brain and disappears if that region is removed.

The mammalian mother usually assists at the birth of her young by biting off the umbilical cord, eating the placenta and licking her young. But sometimes, especially if she is disturbed, she may eat her babies too by mistake. This is the explanation of the domestic tragedies that sometimes occur with tame rats or hamsters.

An ewe that has lost her lamb will accept another only if it has first been covered with the skin of her own dead baby, so that it has the correct smell. The skin can be removed once she has adopted the new lamb. In a similar way, unreconciled at the loss of her calf, a cow when given its stuffed hide for consolation licked and rubbed it fondly. The blindness of instinct is illustrated by the fact that when the cow discovered that the hide was stuffed with straw, she began to eat it! Although mammals may use several senses in everyday life, often a single cue may suffice for recognition.

The majority of mammals are undoubtedly polygamous but a few are believed to pair for life. Thus whereas male and female elephants associate only in the rutting season, the rhinoceros is monogamous and parents and young may stay together for years. In many and especially in polygamous species where the attention of the male is concentrated on keeping his harem together and on repelling rivals, male offspring are regarded with jealousy by their fathers.

Mother weasel removing her young to a place of safety

138

In some carnivores the male parent appears to have little paternal instinct and will eat his babies unless driven off by the female. In wolves, foxes and cougars on the other hand, the male brings food to the lactating female, defends his family and will even care for the young if the mother is killed. The father weasel also provides for the whole of his family. Finally, among polygamous monkeys and apes the overlord male remains with his harem and defends his entire family. Usually however acts of altruism towards the young do not differ from those exhibited to other members of the social group.

Learning and play in mammals

In contrast to birds where instinct plays a greater part in behaviour than does learning, young mammals learn a great deal by *imitating* in play the actions of their parents. Youth is the time

Female shrew leading her 'caravan' of young. These have an innate tendency to hold the tail of the one in front during the first three weeks after birth

for play, when animals perfect the behaviour they will require in later life. It is not mere chance that little girls like to play with dolls, boys with toy soldiers.

Young lions possess a deep-seated hunting instinct — at the zoo you can see them pounce on their mother's tail — and this develops during youth by practice and imitation of adult lions. But they do not lack discipline, a point which might be noted by those who advocate free expression and the absence of restraint in child education. The lion cub who becomes too obstreperous and fails to heed the warning growls of his fond parent may receive a sound cuff which sends him flying! An untrained lion kills clumsily until he has learned otherwise. Indeed buffalo, the most formidable of all prey, is hunted by lions only in certain parts of Africa where the art of tackling them is handed down from old to young by imitation.

Imitation is important too in the learning of birds. Many species of songbird are born with a basic instinctive song to which the trills are added by imitation. Consequently it is not surprising that, in several species, various dialects have sprung up in different parts of the geographical range.

The part played by imitation and learning in the spread of the habit of opening milk bottles by tits is well known. Its significance is not always obvious, however, for the birds do not necessarily steal any cream. Indeed, a friend once described to me how the tits came into her kitchen to peck at some silver bottle caps, quite ignoring the unopened bottles left by the milkman outside the door.

A less well-known habit is diffused among greenfinches. Within the last few years these birds have learned to feed on the fruit of *Daphne mezereum*, a compact shrub that bears a profusion of fragrant blossom in the early spring. A pair of birds, usually, will visit and strip a bush in May and June while the fruits are still green. They can then crack the immature stones and devour the large seeds.

The opening of milk bottles has, of course, arisen only since their introduction, but there is no clear initiating factor in the second case since greenfinches and *Daphne* have probably shared the same geographical range for thousands of years.

Young animals constantly practise their methods of locomotion. Escape and flight are essential and, from an early age, play develops speed in running, flying or swimming. Domestic lambs and kids can often be seen to practice the vertical jumps that stand their mountain-dwelling relations in such good stead.

Otters at play sliding on a snowy slope

Play often includes offensive and defensive movements. Young kittens, badgers, foxes, weasels etc. frequently play at stalking some symbolic victim — a piece of wood or a leaf. Bear cubs, monkeys and apes indulge in wrestling matches and a puppy will shake an old slipper as he would a rabbit.

Social animals tend to play social games. 'Follow my leader' is popular with lambs and sheep and amongst gibbons in the tree tops. Otter cubs and deer indulge in 'hide and seek', while young badgers and red deer often play 'king of the castle'! Adult play is generally concerned with courtship, but otters of all ages seem to enjoy sliding down mud banks, pandas occupy themselves by turning somersaults, porpoises by swimming around a ship.

Play keeps animals occupied when they are in captivity, maintains their muscle tone and provides constant practice for activities essential to life. Not only does play provide an outlet for abundant energy, but it provides the satisfaction of consummating instinctive activities.

Baboons and other monkeys which spend much of their time in open country form large social groups for they are safer in numbers, whereas those that live in forests tend to maintain small and loosely co-ordinated groups. The fact that gibbons do not appear to form social groups can be explained by the same argument, for they live in the tree tops where there are relatively few predators.

Young Hamadryas baboons that have been frightened either flee, or if their alarm is intense they seek out the member of their group who ranks highest in the 'peck order'. When, as is usually the case, the highest-ranking individual is the cause of the fear this does not significantly change the behaviour of the frightened animal. After a subordinate monkey has run to a high-ranking one, its behaviour usually shows unmistakable signs of conflict. Ambivalent postures and screeches show its tendency to run away, yet it continues to sit nearby.

European badgers playing leapfrog

Experiments on the development of affection in infant monkeys shows that the ideal mother, never angry, never cross, can be constructed from 'a block of wood covered by sponge rubber, and sheathed in a terry-cloth skin'. From a psychological point of view, the mother is not essentially a source of food, but of comfort and encouragement to her baby. With advancing age the elements of this behaviour pattern in the relationship with the mother do not vanish but project themselves upon even higher-ranking individuals.

This tendency to run to a leader is often explained by the protection afforded, but the true cause may be the compulsory switching of attention towards animals occupying a particular social position. This observation may shed some light on one aspect of human behaviour. History is replete with examples of man's tendency to line up behind an intimidating leader; a tendency which must be clearly distinguished from democratic methods of delegating authority to a leader for a social task. It has been suggested that this instinctive tendency may control human behaviour without one becoming aware of what has happened. If so, to become aware of instinctive social motivation will help in the development of greater personal freedom.

Types of learning

In conclusion, the main types of learning found in animals can be summarised as follows:

(*a*) *Habituation* — learning not to respond to a stimulus that ceases to be of significance, thereby avoiding a considerable waste of energy (see p. 24).

(*b*) *Conditioning and association learning* — modification of a reflex or instinctive act by experience, so that the original stimulus is replaced by another although the response remains the same (see p. 25).

(*c*) *Trial-and-error learning* — often achieved as a result of play, trial-and-error learning depends upon rewards or punishments being derived from exploratory, appetitive behaviour. It is the type of learning that results in the solution of puzzles. An example of trial-and-error learning is afforded by the fact that the response of dogs to the smell of meat is not innate, for puppies reared on milk do not salivate when first shown meat. However, they soon learn to associate the smell with the food. It has been shown too that the presence of some fur is necessary for young foxes first to respond to meat.

(*d*) *Imprinting* — this type of learning is that most frequently combined with instinctive behaviour. It is of short duration, often almost irreversible and acquired before the reaction itself is established. It is usually exhibited in response to a *'releaser'* (see p. 61).

(e) *Latent learning* — latent learning, like imprinting, is acquired before the animal obtains any benefit from it. As in the case of some trial-and-error learning, it results from curiosity. For example, rats allowed the freedom of a maze can later solve problems offering a food reward more quickly than can rats that have not explored the maze. In a similar way, wild animals often learn the features of their territories long before such knowledge is of value to them. Again, latent learning is frequently achieved as the result of play.

(f) *Insight learning* — whereas insight is concerned with the organisation of perceptions and has been defined as 'the apprehension of relations', insight learning is the sudden production of a new response by the 'adaptive reorganisation of experience'. Insight and insight learning are characteristic of human thought, but they also occur to some extent in sub-human animals. Examples are afforded by the chimpanzee who managed to fit one piece of bamboo into another to make a long stick with which he was able to knock down a banana hanging from the roof of his cage, and the cat who, without previous experimentation, pulled towards him by means of the string to which it was tied, food that was otherwise beyond reach.*

In thought, the brain works by comparing the configuration of stimuli received through the sense-organs with a series of models already learned. One of the first lessons a baby learns is to focus its eyes, to follow lines and to distinguish between solid objects and shadows. Only later does it learn to recognise objects by sight. During the years of childhood, when the eyes are constantly exploring the surroundings, a series of models is built up within the brain and these are later used to compare and select significant features of visual experience.

* An eminent botanist relates that on a collecting expedition in tropical forest, he employed a tame monkey to gather epiphytic orchids from the upper branches of the trees. One day he saw some magnificent orchids growing on some lianas that hung down a vertical cliff. He told the monkey to climb down for them, but it refused and neither bribe nor entreaty would persuade it to go. The poor botanist was feeling quite desperate when at last the monkey relented, shrugged its shoulders, and began to pull up the lianas hand over fist!

Chapter 12

Displacement activity and human behaviour

> When we turn to less common gestures in ourselves,
> which we are accustomed to look at as artificial or con-
> ventional, — such as shrugging the shoulders, as a sign
> of impotence, or the raising the arms with open hands
> and extended fingers, as a sign of wonder, — we feel
> perhaps too much surprise at finding that they are
> innate.
>
> CHARLES DARWIN (1872)

IT WAS a lovely sunny afternoon in July, 1944. A squadron of British Cromwell tanks was advancing slowly across a corn-field south of Caen towards a small wood. German infantry were hiding in the corn all round us: we fired at them with machine-guns and high explosive, and took many prisoners. We were ourselves shelled and mortared heavily the whole time. Then, as a number of German 'Tigers' (whose big 88 mm. guns could make mincemeat of the smaller British cruiser tanks) were reported approaching, we entered the wood, our Cromwells facing outwards in all directions, to await the onslaught.

The shelling continued, and several of our tanks were hit. The explosions were deafeningly close, and, although the air reeked of cordite and petrol, I thought it wiser to close the turret flaps in case a shell should fall inside. Despite the fact that all our lives de-pended upon my remaining alert, oddly enough I could scarcely keep my eyes open, and my driver and wireless-operator were snoring audibly.

This curious desire for sleep before and during lulls in battle was no new experience to me. In the desert many of us had noticed the same phenomenon, and jokingly suggested it was due to relief at no longer being chivvied about by senior officers before the battle began! It was not till some time later that I realised its true significance.

145

It has often been remarked that, under certain conditions, animals may sometimes perform quite irrelevant movements. For example, fighting starlings may stop to preen their feathers, fighting rats groom themselves, courting birds of paradise wipe their bills on the ground as though they were feeding, and fighting cocks will pick up imaginary food. A common tern, whose eggs had been painted blue, pecked them and then went off to bathe and preen herself. Herring gulls and oyster-catchers may be seen to pluck at nesting material whilst engaged in deadly combat. A solitary wasp, thwarted by having repeatedly to remove pebbles placed in the mouth of her burrow, eventually gives up the unequal struggle and runs round in small circles.

As we have seen, instincts are motivated in the first place by internal changes in the animal. These may arise spontaneously, as in the case of the oestrus cycles of mammals, and the feeding re-actions of lug-worms; or they may be induced by external agencies such as changing day length which influences the breeding cycle in birds. Such internal changes often involve the ductless-glands. The pituitary, for instance, may secrete more of the hormone which stimulates the sex-glands.

These internal changes in turn affect the behaviour of the ani-mal. At this stage of the behaviour pattern, it will often wander about at random as though seeking some outlet. This is the phase of '*appetitive behaviour*' which has been described as 'the variable introductory phase of an instinctive behaviour pattern or sequence'. Finally, the animal reaches a situation in which a '*consummatory act*' or series of such acts can be carried out. These release the nervous tension built up within the animal, for the performance of such acts is usually followed by a decline in '*drive*' or motivation as measured by the amount of stimulus necessary to induce it to repeat the behaviour pattern.

When an animal is under the influence of a powerful urge, but is prevented from expressing it in the normal way, it may perform some other, apparently irrelevant, act. This is known as '*displace-ment activity*', and occurs, for example, when the instinct to flee conflicts with the instinct to fight.

Displacement activities usually result, either from a conflict between two strongly activated but antagonistic drives, or from strong motivation, usually sexual, in the absence of the necessary stimulus required for the release of the consummatory act. In either case the drive is thwarted and impulses obstructed so that nervous energy is prevented from being discharged in the normal way. However, by means of displacement activity, nervous tension may still be reduced.

Reactions which can reasonably be interpreted as displacement activities may also occur where there is merely too much motivation. The fighting cocks mentioned above may have picked up imaginary food, not because they felt simultaneous conflicting desires to flee and to fight, but because they were under the influence of such intense 'emotion' that the normal outlet by fighting was insufficient to release all their nervous energy.

During the mating season, if a male stickleback meets another on his territory, he chases it away. Outside his territory he avoids a fight and will flee if attacked or threatened, but on the boundary between two territories, fierce fighting may take place. This is often interrupted by threat behaviour during which the rival males adopt

Displacement preening by shelldrake before mating

a vertical, head-downward posture similar to that normally employed in digging a nesting hole. In cases of intense stimulation actual digging may take place. It has been suggested that the threat posture results from the 'ritualisation' of a displacement reaction.

A complex instinct, such as reproduction, as we have seen, is composed of an hierarchy of simpler instincts. Consequently, if the consummation of an instinctive act at the top of the hierarchy is prevented, displacement activity often takes the form of an instinctive act of lower rank. Indeed, when faced with some predicament, an animal will frequently take refuge in the form of some easy familiar movement that has no connection with the problem at all. Similarly, children bursting out of school often perform various strenuous displacement activities which release their frustrated pent-up energy.

It is possible that in conflict situations two drives such as attack and escape may mutually inhibit each other and thereby remove the inhibitory effect each of them normally has on all other behaviour patterns. The latter, although weakly activated, will thus be able to give rise to movement: and whatever other stimuli are present may decide on the form the displacement activity will take.

Many birds, when disturbed or thwarted, react by breaking into song. In a similar way, small boys may whistle in aggressive self-assertion, and when a man regresses to this juvenile practice, it is often in situations of suspense, tension or surprise. Perhaps hysterical laughter, too, may sometimes result from the fatigue caused by an excess of conscious thought.

Another result from a conflict of drives may be 're-directed' activity: this is activity directed towards an object other than that arousing it. For example, a man may bang the table when he is irritated by his wife, because he is inhibited from striking her! Similarly a gull may re-direct an attack towards the ground or some inanimate object. Cases in which a bird attacks its mate or an inoffensive individual of another species may be due to the fact that the other cannot help providing some of the stimuli that normally release attack (p. 56) and which are optimally provided by a rival male. But the worried husband who snaps out at his wife may have been aroused by a man higher in social rank whom he cannot answer back. Similarly a child may bully a younger brother or sister when he is prevented from doing what he wants, because he dare not attack the adult causing his annoyance.

Displacement activities have reached their highest development in birds whose behaviour is composed largely of rigid instincts. They have a biological advantage in that a displacement-prone species can more readily modify its behaviour to suit changed circumstances, and is, therefore, better adapted than one which does not show so much displacement activity. Much bird display consists of displacement activities that have later become ritualised. Thus the posture that the male heron assumes to attract the female to his territory is similar to that used in catching fish. The gadwall exhibits to its mate a display in which displacement-preening and displacement-drinking follow one another in sequence and the mandarin duck performs a similar ceremonial in which the order is reversed. In cranes and pigeons, a movement of the head towards the wing, which evidently originated as displacement-preening, functions in the one species as a threat signal, in the other as sexual display.

In mammals, where learning plays a much greater part in

behaviour and instinct a correspondingly smaller one, displacement activities are less marked and more smoothly ritualised into display and signal movements. Man is one of the least instinctive of animals and insight plays an important rôle in his behaviour. He has, nevertheless, a number of basic instincts concerned especially with feeding and reproduction as well as other lesser instincts. For example, the touch stimulus of an insect crawling over the hand releases a quick movement to throw it off. This reaction is innate and matures late in the development of the individual for it is not found in very young children.

Sleep, too, is a true instinctive act depending upon stimulation of a centre in the hypothalamus of the brain (see p. 51). In situations resulting in mild conflict of low intensity it may take the form of displacement-yawning, but at times of extreme tension such as arise in warfare, there may be an almost unsurmountable inclination to go to sleep. This is the probable explanation of the phenomenon mentioned at the beginning of this chapter. In some birds such as avocets and oyster-catchers, sleep also forms an outlet in situations where fear and the aggressive instinct conflict with one another.

Some people find an instinctive desire to pass water at times of stress such as during examinations or when waiting to be interviewed. Others literally feel sick at the prospect of an unpleasant ordeal. Scratching occurs as an innate displacement activity amongst apes and the human displacement reactions of scratching the head, stroking the chin and so on when puzzled or bewildered are probably instinctive. In women, they usually take the form of adjusting the coiffure or powdering the face even when such attentions are dictated, neither by the requirements of comfort nor of appearance.

Since so much of human behaviour is learned, it is not surprising that many displacement activities should take the form of learned movements such as fidgeting with a key chain or other object, smoking a cigarette and so on. It may be that many scientific, artistic and other creative endeavours are really the result of displacement activity engendered by the conflict between primitive instinct and social and moral convention; in which case such outlets may be infinitely more satisfactory than the simple consummatory acts they have supplanted.

Displacement reactions may also initiate the subconscious learning of bad habits and it is sometimes very difficult to break them later on. Human behaviour is so complex that useful generalities cannot be made to cover such varied manifestations of habit as smoking, drinking, nail-biting, stuttering and so on. Indeed so many elements may be involved in these complex behaviour patterns that the best way of breaking one set of bad habits may turn out to be the worst method of tackling another. Some of the clearest evidence about the relative efficiency of different methods comes from studies, such as those of the fears of young children. These methods include: *'counter-conditioning'* — presenting the feared object together with a reward such as a sweet; *'exhaustion'* — forcing the child to remain in a feared situation and ignoring his fears; *'change of environment'* — ensuring that the feared object is not met so that the reaction disappears by disuse, and *'social imitation'* — that is, association with other children who do not share the same fear.

Of these, the most effective are undoubtedly counter-conditioning and social imitation.

Social responses in man

The social responses of man are affected, not only by his individual experiences, but also by the age at which these occur. Children who are separated from their mothers between the ages of six months and three years often undergo intense emotional disturbances in which rage and despair alternate, before they settle down, the social relationships having been organised on a new pattern. If this new psychopathic organisation has time to consolidate, as it does between three and five years of age, it tends to become permanent. Thus, lasting harm may result from lengthy separation from one or both parents: it may be very difficult for a child to accept a father from whom he has been separated during these critical years.

The social responses of the adult are extremely complex and sophisticated. Nothing so simple and dramatic as imprinting occurs in man. Indeed, human personality is an exceptionally difficult subject to study scientifically. Nevertheless, it is believed that many important social responses result from an inner drive seeking discharge in a consummatory act which results in a release of tension. The drive to make a love relation with the parents is innate in children as in other mammals and birds.

The selection of a lover in adult life may be strongly influenced by the character of the individual's early love object, a process which may be carried to the point of fixation. Instinctive behaviour generally passes through critical phases of development, and adult sexual responses, as is well known, often utilise in a new configuration the social responses of childhood. There is clearly a parallel here with the mating reactions of birds and the bond that binds the dog to his master. Finally, the discharge of instinctive energy by means of displacement activities indicates a basic similarity underlying human behaviour and that of other animals.

Most people are familiar with the classical experiment in which a dog was taught to salivate at the sound of a bell. By presenting food and ringing the bell simultaneously, a *conditioned reflex* was set up. After this, salivation occurred whenever the bell sounded and even though no food was present. In a similar way a three-year old boy has had a *phobia* or neurotic fear of rabbits induced in him. Every time he reached out to touch a tame rabbit, a loud noise was made by banging an iron bar with a hammer. In consequence, a conditioned fear of furry animals developed so that the unfortunate child would not tolerate such creatures in the same room as himself.

Afterwards the phobia was cured by introducing the rabbit only at a great distance from the child who was simultaneously given chocolate. Gradually the fear response was abolished altogether and the boy's natural love of furry animals returned.

Although man, considered as an individual, is undoubtedly a social animal the relations between one society and another are often on a level that is barely more than sub-social! Two familiar and fundamental principles can be seen to colour nearly every political and international scene: the struggle for existence and the necessity for co-operation.

Man is aggressive and shows hierarchies like the 'peck orders' of chickens, but this does not prove that warfare is an innate behaviour pattern. And even if it were, instinctive behaviour can often be altered as in the case of civilised marriage customs. If not innate, war has certainly become, through the centuries, a learned pattern of human behaviour. It may perhaps be related to a genuine territorial instinct.

Group aggression

At this point a distinction should be drawn between individual and group aggression. The latter seems to be closely associated with the fundamental type of social behaviour in which, as we have seen (p. 127), each individual in a group does what the others do. For example, a flock of sheep may be scattered over a hillside as they graze, but on the approach of a man they respond by running into a compact group. Similar behaviour on the part of the American bison assisted greatly in their wholesale slaughter during the last century. In wolves, Cape hunting-dogs, and other social carnivores, such *'allelomimetic'* behaviour may be associated with fighting and aggression. The animals frequently combine in hunting activities; and if a lone wolf approaches the den of a well-organised pack he is attacked by the whole group and driven away. The same tendency can be seen among social groups of monkeys.

Co-ordinated aggression enables the group to become much more powerful and dangerous than a number of scattered individuals would be and, in man too, has no doubt played an important part in evolution.

In an attempt to study the development of group aggression, the members of a boys' camp were set co-operative tasks of such a nature that they did not lead to competition, frustration or conflict within the group. A similar camp was established nearby whose occupants also had a well-developed team spirit, and the two groups managed in such a way as to produce bad feeling between them. All contact was prevented except in competitive situations, and a tournament organised in which one side won all the prizes. Frustration led to aggression and the boys soon began to raid each others camps and to fight if they met accidentally.

When, however, a situation occurred which provided a threat to both groups — the water supply to each camp failed — the two groups worked together and mutual aggression was greatly reduced. The results of this experiment do suggest that man's aggressive nature may be curbed by cultural methods that reduce the social causes of aggression or direct them into harmless and pleasurable channels such as team games and creative recreations.

The problems of the individual

Unfortunately the study of behaviour cannot always provide a guide where human problems of an ethical nature are concerned. Each of us, in the last resort, is compelled to be subjective in deciding his course of action. Most people would agree that war is morally wrong, but they rightly consider cruelty, bad faith, and the suppression of freedom to be even greater evils.

Often in life one is forced to make decisions subjectively when logic, science or materialism provide no guidance. Man, like many other animals, possesses two incompatible drives; the one self-centred, the other altruistic and social. He has to decide which is to guide his actions. Freed from the tyranny of instinct* as a result of the dominance of reason, or *insight learning* in our behaviour, we are faced with the problem of free will. Unlike other social animals, we cannot rely blindly upon the guidance of instincts that are opposed to the demands of the society in which we belong.

Consequently, we are forced to test every impulse by conscious thought, to find out if we can yield to it without harming the cultural values of our society. Hence there is a conflict between our simple, but often by no means ignoble, instincts, and our deeper insight. To some extent freedom is inevitably surrendered as the price of the security and the aesthetic and cultural advantages of civilisation.

On the one hand it is not always possible to ignore instinct, and reason may be weak when confronted by really powerful motivation. Who has not allowed the impulse of the moment to outweigh better judgment? Falling in love changes one's entire outlook on life and it is said that many crimes, including murder, are committed in an instinctive urge to 'show off'. On the other hand, those who repress their instincts too strongly, may involve themselves in neuroses!

Despite instinct and environmental influences there is much scope in human behaviour for free will. Naturally freedom is limited; however, just as we cannot drive a car everywhere yet can select between the high road and the low, so we can use our instincts creatively in the best sense, or we may consummate them crudely and selfishly. The choice lies with everyone.

> 'Duty has to be faced; nothing was ever won by shirking an issue or shrinking from an obligation.'
> E. H. H. ALLENBY (1936)

* P. Ovidi Nasonis (43 B.C.–A.D. 17) *Metamorphoseon*, Lib. 1.
  Os homini sublime dedit caelumque videre
  iussit et erectos ad sidere tollere vultus.

Bibliography

ALLEE, W. C., 1951. *Cooperation among animals*. Revised Ed. New York.

*ARMSTRONG, E. A., 1947. *Bird display and behaviour*. London.

BIERENS DE HAAN, J. A., 1947. *Animal psychology*. London.

BORRADAILE, L. A., 1923. *The animal and its environment*. London.

BOULIÈRE, F., 1955. *The natural history of mammals*. London.

BUDDENBROCK, W. VON, 1956. *The love-life of animals*. London.

BURTON, M., 1950. *Animals and their behaviour*. London.

——, 1953. *Animal courtship*. London.

*CARTHY, J. D., 1958. *An introduction to the behaviour of invertebrates*. London.

CLOUDSLEY-THOMPSON, J. L., 1958. *Spiders, scorpions, centipedes and mites*. London.

*COTT, H. B., 1957. *Adaptive coloration in animals*. 2nd Ed. London.

*FRAENKEL, G. S. & GUNN, D. L., 1940. *The orientation of animals*. Oxford.

FRISCH, K. VON, 1954. *The dancing bees*. London.

*HEAPE, W., 1931. *Emigration, migration and nomadism*. Cambridge.

*HEDIGER, H., 1955. *Studies of the psychology and behaviour of animals in zoos and circuses*. London.

IMMS, A. D., 1938. *Social behaviour in insects*. 2nd Ed. London.

KATZ, D., 1953. *Animals and man*. Revised Ed. London.

*KENDEIGH, S. C., 1952. *Parental care and its evolution in birds*. Urbana, Illinois.

KÖHLER, W., 1957. *The mentality of apes*. 2nd Ed. London.

LANE, F. W., 1955. *Nature parade*. 4th Ed. London.

LORENZ, K. Z., 1952. *King Solomon's ring. New light on animal ways*. London.

*MARSHALL, A. J., 1954. *Bower birds. Their displays and breeding cycles*. Oxford.

MILNE, L. J. & M. J., 1955. *The mating instinct*. London.

NOBLE, R. C., 1950. *The nature of the beast*. London.

PYCRAFT, W. P., 1913. *The courtship of animals*. 3rd Ed. London.

*RIBBANDS, C. R., 1953. *The behaviour and social life of honeybees*. London.

RICHARDS, O. W., 1953. *The social insects*. London.

RUSSELL, E. S., 1946. *The behaviour of animals*. 2nd Ed. Rep. London.

SAVORY, T. H., 1960. *Instinctive living*. London.

*SCHILLER, C. H., (ed.), 1957. *Instinctive behaviour. The development of a modern concept*. New York.

*SCOTT, J. P., 1958. *Animal behaviour*. Chicago.

——, 1958. *Aggression*. Chicago.

*Thorpe, W. H., 1956. *Learning and instinct in animals*. London.
*Tinbergen, N., 1951. *The study of instinct*. London.
——, 1953. *Social behaviour in animals with special reference to vertebrates.*
    London.
Wells, G. P., 1955. *The sources of animal behaviour*. London.
Young, J. Z., 1951. *Doubt and certainty in science*. Oxford.
**Physiological mechanisms in animal behaviour*. 1950. (Ed. J. F. Danielli
    & R. Brown.) *Symp. Soc. Exp. Biol.*, No. IV. Cambridge.
**Rhythmic and synthetic processes in growth*. 1957. (Ed. D. Rudnick.) *15th
    Growth Symposium*. Princeton, New Jersey.

* Advanced works

Index